Relief from Anxiety and Panic

"The effectiveness of this program lies in its simplicity. In essence you learn two simple things: one is a different perspective on breathing, and the other is how to gently nudge your breathing to how it should be. The benefits are profound." — AMANDA FERRY, BSc (Psych) PGDip Psych

"In my opinion, this is the best self-help book for overcoming chronic anxiety and panic - and I have read lots of them. With clarity, simplicity and empathy, the author shows how to use healthy breathing to take back control of how your body functions. Use this book to calm your breathing, your body and your mind." — KAREN ST CLAIR, Counsellor

"This book changed my life. For the first time I became aware of what dysfunctional breathing is, and of what it does to perpetuate the out-of-the-blue attacks of terror I have suffered for decades. I have not felt this sense of inner peace in a very long time." — MICHELLE TAJA MILLER, BA (Psychology)

"This book gives comprehensive and enlightening information on anxiety and panic disorders and their connection with faulty 'everyday' breathing. It offers a self-management solution using the scientifically-based principles of Breathing Retraining which are deceptively simple and easy to follow. I love the 'cloud exercise'. This concept is a visual and easy to manage tool that immediately offers relief of acute symptoms." — GLENN SMITH, Physiotherapist

relief from anxiety *and* panic

by changing how you breathe

TESS GRAHAM

BSc. Grad Dip Physio

BreatheAbility Publications Canberra Australia

Limits of Liability and Disclaimer
This book is for informational and educational purposes only and should not be construed as, relied upon, or substituted for, medical or psychological advice. You should consult your doctor before undertaking any change to your health management, medication or other prescribed treatments.

The purpose of this book is to educate and empower. While the author has used reasonable efforts to ensure the information contained in this book is accurate and up to date the author makes no warranties or representations as to the accuracy of the information. The author provides no guarantee or promise regarding the effects on their health of anyone following these ideas, suggestions, strategies, exercises and techniques. The author shall have neither liability nor responsibility to anyone for any loss or damage arising from, or alleged to have arisen from, directly or indirectly, any use or misuse of the information or suggestions in this book.

Cover and interior design by Deborah Bradseth of Tugboat Design (USA)

Illustrations/Figures 6.3, 11.2, 13.1, 15.1, 18.1, 19.1
From Relief from Snoring and Sleep Apnoea by Tess Graham
Copyright © Penguin Group (Australia) 2012
Reprinted by permission of Penguin Random House Australia Pty Limited

All other illustrations by Mat Colley, Foundry (Australia)

National Library of Australia
Cataloguing-in-Publication entry (pbk):

Graham, Tess, author.
Relief from Anxiety and Panic: by changing how you breathe / Tess Graham.
ISBN: 978-0-9954127-0-5 (paperback)

Notes: Includes bibliographical references.

Breathing exercises – Therapeutic use.
Anxiety – Treatment.
Panic attacks – Treatment.

TessGraham.com

Issued also in electronic format

CONTENTS

FOREWORD

By Dr Antoinette Harmer, Clinical Psychologist

It is my pleasure to introduce this latest book from Tess Graham. As a practitioner of clinical psychology for over 20 years, I have repeatedly encountered clients and practitioners alike who can benefit from sound knowledge and simple and effective practices regarding how we breathe.

In our clinic, I can comfortably say that every client we see could benefit from better breathing. I regularly observe poor breathing habits - holding the breath for many seconds without awareness, yawning when not feeling tired, gasping or taking gulping breaths, audible breathing and rapid, shallow breathing ... and this can be observed in normal, non-anxious conversation!

While health professionals generally acknowledge the importance of breathing for 'stress management', it is not common practice to truly understand the physiology of breathing and how critical a 'normal' breathing pattern is for general health. We teach our clients breathing exercises to help them cope with a panic attack or to calm down when stressed. However few people suffering from anxiety will be aware of their usual, 'everyday' breathing.

People simply don't understand that the way they breathe throughout the day, between attacks, can be what sets them up for chronic anxiety, a heightened stress response or panic attack. And that is one problem.

Another is the alarming misunderstanding amongst fellow practitioners of what healthy breathing is. It is common to hear psychology and related practitioners talk about deep breathing, and to teach their clients what they were taught ... "take long deep breaths". We aren't taught to understand the physiology and biochemistry of breathing, nor the critical importance of posture, nose breathing and maintaining the correct balance of oxygen and carbon dioxide in the lungs and bloodstream. We don't see dysfunctional breathing in our clients (unless they are having a panic attack) because we don't know what to look for. In summary, we don't have the knowledge to teach effective breathing to our clients.

Tess Graham has dedicated her career to understanding optimal breathing and teaching others. Her commitment is palpable and inspiring. While her first book, *Relief from Snoring and Sleep Apnoea*, addressed sleep and anxiety difficulties alike, it is wonderful to see a dedicated book that directly speaks to people with anxiety difficulties. It provides its readers with knowledge, insight, self-awareness and a means to self-empowerment.

While breathing more effectively is not the complete treatment for anxiety or other psychological or physiological disorders, it is an essential grounding. It costs nothing, is easy to do once you know how and can become automatic very quickly. People can then more effectively make use of psychological interventions and lifestyle changes to complete their mastery over their anxiety experiences.

Tess writes in a relaxed and empowering way that comfortably and efficiently walks the reader through building their awareness and knowledge, and developing the nine healthy breathing habits that they can effortlessly assimilate into their lifestyle.

Many of my clients have done breathing retraining with Tess. It is fabulous to see this book in print and making her work more widely available. The knowledge she imparts and the way she has organised this book will enable many more people to benefit from her knowledge, experience and expertise. I know Tess's book will be a regular recommendation for our clients.

Enjoy and breathe well.

— Dr Antoinette Harmer, Clinical Psychologist
Clinical Director, Capital Anxiety Clinic and
Optimal Health & Performance, Canberra

INTRODUCTION

This book can transform your life. It can guide you to triumph over anxiety in a way that is so simple, so common sense, that it has been overlooked.

The book evolved out of the urgings of many I have worked with over the last two decades, to share this information with others who struggle with debilitating anxiety. It is both educational and practical. It offers you an opportunity to get to the heart of the biochemical and physiological disturbance in your body that fuels the mental torture and physical discomfort you may live with daily. It explains dysfunctional breathing, how dramatically it affects the way your body functions, and what to do about it through breathing retraining. Yes, you can change the way you breathe. And that changes the way you feel.

Breathing dysfunction – breathing that is 'physiologically abnormal' – is a major and consistent contributor to anxiety disorders that is often unobserved or disregarded in medical management. If you don't fix it, then other treatments are compromised. Breathing retraining is a science-based, simple, practical, and easy-to-do process that has been used successfully by thousands of people to get rapid, profound and lasting relief from anxiety and other breathing-related conditions.

The teachings in this book are not *New Age* fluff. They are based on long-established (but neglected) medical science, and on extensive clinical practice. I have been particularly influenced by the teachings of Ukrainian-born doctor, Konstantin P. Buteyko (1923–2003) and Canadian-born dentist, Weston A. Price (1870–1948). Buteyko, a renowned physiologist, researcher and medical doctor, devoted over 40 years to restoring mental and physical health through correcting breathing dysfunction. Price, from his studies of isolated, traditionally healthy populations, formulated the dietary principles necessary to support good breathing and physical and mental health.

Breathing retraining over 20 years ago freed two of my children from the grip of recurring asthma and led me to establish a clinical practice as a physiotherapist, devoted entirely to helping people breathe better, in order to be, feel and sleep better. Today, people with anxiety and sleep disorders make up more than 85 per cent of those who attend the breathing clinic.

How the book works best

The book is set out to cover topics and practices in much the same order as the breathing programs I have taught successfully for over two decades. There are tables and charts that you can fill out in the book or you can download a free workbook from www.BreatheAbility.com/store/. The book is best followed in sequence, from beginning to end. That, from my experience, is what works best. Concepts are explained first, then practical follows. You have to know what is going on first before you 'get' the solution. The first practical starts in Chapter 5; I expect you will feel the first improvements immediately.

This style of breathing retraining shows extraordinary and consistent success. It takes into account our time-poor, fast-paced world and the sense of overwhelm and pressure that envelops many anxiety sufferers. While simple and not requiring strict discipline or rigorous training, it does require some attention from you to establish a better pattern of breathing. However, the first positive results are often noticed within minutes and you will be shown how to blend breathing retraining into your usual daily activities. You will see that small adjustments to your breathing each day can transform your life.

The book is peppered with examples, stories, case studies, and 'before and after' figures gathered from over 6,000 people who have attended my courses. The names and some situations I have used are fictitious; the experiences are real. I hope they will enlighten, inspire and reassure you that you are not alone and that you are not 'a hopeless case'. They demonstrate that improving the way you breathe, and freeing yourself from anxiety and panic attacks, are eminently doable, and greatly rewarding.

Important note

Breathing retraining to improve dysfunctional breathing is inherently safe. However, if you have any serious mental or physical illness requiring ongoing treatment or medication, you should always consult your doctor before undertaking any change to your health management, including undergoing breathing retraining. Any changes to medication and other prescribed treatments should only be undertaken under the supervision and with the consent of a medical doctor.

PART ONE

UNDERSTANDING ANXIETY AND PANIC: THE WAY YOU BREATHE, THE WAY YOU FEEL

'Life is a perpetual instruction in cause and effect.'

RALPH WALDO EMERSON

CHAPTER 1

Anxiety – a new understanding, a practical solution

Anxiety is an experience familiar to almost everyone, as we try to cope with the stresses and complexities of modern life. But we aren't all anxious to the same degree. Anxiety is a serious problem for about 25 per cent of the adult population at some time in their lives. As it was for Helena.

Helena's life was on hold for over 10 years after she suffered what in retrospect she saw as a fairly minor event. She lost her job when the firm she worked for downsized. But at the time, Helena took it personally; losing her job meant she was 'not good enough', not useful.

She had experienced minor anxiety for most of her life but this event caused her to feel near-constant anxiety, with terrifying panic attacks and fear of crowds, open spaces and social situations, and some frightening physical symptoms. These included tingling in her face and limbs, severe shortness of breath, heart palpitations and chest pains. It seemed she was locked out of life: she couldn't work; she couldn't go outside her home except on the arm of her husband or her sister, and even then an increased and all-consuming fear might abort the excursion. Helena had been told that no-one dies from a panic attack, but she sure felt as though she might. Anti-anxiety medications initially provided some relief but then stopped helping. Cognitive behavioural therapy seemed promising, but she cancelled more appointments than she kept. Helena's story continues later in this chapter.

Like most anxiety sufferers, you probably at times feel despondent about the future, and helpless and afraid because of the physical and mental symptoms you wrestle with daily. Like Helena, anxiety may have completely taken over your life. Your life and your world may feel compressed.

Anxiety is most commonly seen as a manifestation of wayward emotions, or an imbalance in brain chemistry, or habitual negative thinking, or a situation of fear or threat, or a tangle of several of these. Most people are advised to medicate their anxiety or manage it through controlling their thoughts and 're-wiring their brains'. Thankfully, with the awareness we have today of mental health issues, people are less likely to be told, "Just pull yourself together!"

While pharmaceutical and psychological interventions are important in the treatment of anxiety disorders, medications may not always be effective in the long term, and therapy is not always possible for as often or as long as it takes.

A BREAKTHROUGH APPROACH – BREATHING RETRAINING

There is another way to get fast and lasting relief from anxiety, but you may not have heard of it.

Breathing retraining addresses a major aspect of anxiety disorders that pharmaceutical and psychological therapies do not. It addresses the disturbance in physiology – that is, normal body function, caused by an abnormal or 'dysfunctional' pattern of breathing.

An abnormal breathing pattern switches on the 'fight-or-flight' centre in the brain and keeps it activated, escalating feelings of anxiety with no relief. This brain centre has a job to do. It warns you of danger so that you can protect yourself. But when this part of the nervous system is constantly on, you may feel in danger most of the time.

MISSED DIAGNOSIS

If you suffer from an anxiety disorder, the first thing to know is that you are not breathing correctly. All the time, not just during an acute episode. Your usual, everyday, or 'baseline' way of breathing is dysfunctional – that is abnormal. You likely are not aware of it. Faulty breathing habits can be as significant as they are subtle. They are not the only thing going on, but are at the root of the disturbance in body chemistry that sets off the cascade of mental and physical symptoms classic in people suffering an anxiety disorder. You are excused for not knowing this, because unfortunately, screening for a dysfunctional breathing pattern is not part of standard medical diagnosis.

The good news is, when you are alert to faulty breathing, you can not only control your breathing and relieve acute symptoms, but you can *normalise* your baseline pattern of breathing. With that comes stable body chemistry, optimal oxygen delivery to your brain and every cell in your body and a calm nervous system, no longer stuck in the fight-or-flight state. You can become cool, calm and in control, on the inside as well as the outside. You can achieve a level of wellbeing you might only have dreamed of. It is not complicated. You usually feel benefits immediately.

As Helena did. When she first phoned me for an appointment, I noticed gasping inhales when she began a sentence. I briefly explained what over-breathing means and gave her a simple instruction to very gently cut back on her air consumption over the next 24 hours. She was immediately won over by her growing sense of calm and control. The next day she kept her appointment with me, and she kept improving. Within two weeks, she felt ready to get out in the world again and start doing the things she used to enjoy.

YOUR JOURNEY BEGINS

The first step towards change and relief is knowing what needs to change. Identifying just how your breathing pattern differs from normal, healthy breathing lights the way back to better breathing habits and a life free of anxiety and panic attacks.

Breathing Quiz

How do you breathe?

Have you ever had your *baseline breathing pattern* checked?

Complete Table 1.1 to find out. Put today's date in the Assessment 1 column. Now put a '1' in each box in the column where the answer is 'yes'. Put a '2' there if it's a *big* yes. Leave blank if it doesn't apply to you. Add up the numbers to get your *dysfunctional breathing score.*

Put a bookmark in this page so you can find it easily when the text refers back to it.

TABLE 1.1: BREATHING PATTERN SELF-ASSESSMENT

BREATHING PARAMETER	**ASSESSMENT 1** **Date:**	**ASSESSMENT 2** **Date:**	**ASSESSMENT 3** **Date:**
Is your breathing heavy, laboured or restricted?			
Do you feel you can't take a satisfying breath?			
Is your breathing uneven or erratic?			
Do you cough (dry) or clear your throat frequently?			
Do you sigh, yawn or take deep breaths often? Estimate number of sighs, yawns, etc., per day	[ ]	[ ]	[ ]
Is your breathing audible day or night?			
Do you mouth breathe during the day?			
Do you mouth breathe with activity?			
Do you mouth breathe during sleep?			
Do you breathe with your upper chest?			
Do you breathe more than 14 times a minute?			
Is your breathing obvious to others?			
DYSFUNCTIONAL BREATHING SCORE			
RESTING HEART RATE			

If you answered 'yes' to even one or two of these indicators of faulty breathing, then read on. Prepare for your life to change.

First you need to check two more things that are connected with your breathing pattern.

POSTURE

Don't move! Or if you just did after seeing the word 'posture', please move back to your usual sitting posture. Now, without moving your torso, place the thumb of one hand on the lower end of your breastbone and the little finger of the same hand on your navel. With an upright posture, there is usually a full stretched hand span between these two points. With a slumped posture, these two points are brought closer together, with a folding or wrinkling effect of the abdomen. If you are seated on a dining chair at the moment, also check yourself in your usual sitting posture in a lounge chair.

Is your posture slumped or upright? ______________________

FIGURE 1.1: IS YOUR POSTURE SLUMPED OR UPRIGHT?

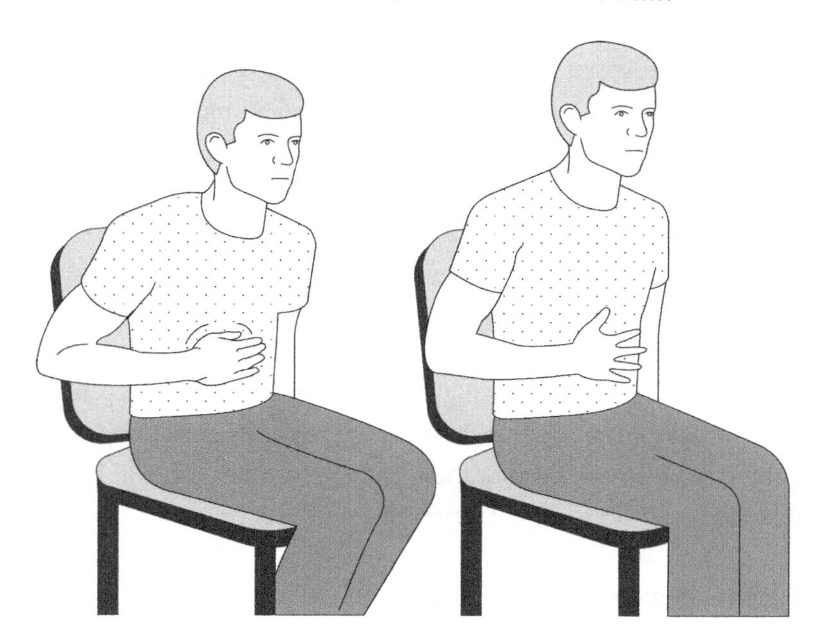

HEART RATE OR PULSE

Heart rate is sometimes considered an indicator of clinical anxiety, and your breathing affects your heart rate. Just how and why will become clearer later. Here we are just getting a baseline 'resting' heart rate for you, and you will be checking it again later as you improve your breathing.

Taking your pulse: You count the pulse on the thumb side of the inside of your wrist 1–2 cm below the crease line at the base of your hand, and one cm from the edge of your wrist. Use two fingers from your other hand and place them gently in the position where you feel the slight throb of the heartbeat.

Count the number of beats, or pulses, in one minute and record it in Table 1.1.

Note: You are checking your baseline breathing pattern, not diagnosing an anxiety disorder or a breathing disorder. Only a medical doctor is qualified to diagnose these. You are identifying faulty breathing habits that may well underlie anxiety and breathing problems.

Change your breathing, change your physiology

How you breathe affects your blood and brain chemistry and your body's stress response. The secret to living a calm and relaxed life is not by going to a retreat centre on a remote tropical island or a far-off mountaintop. It is in how you take your next breath, and the ones after it; every breath you take.

This book will give you everything you need to improve the way you breathe, just as it has given thousands of others. You will learn the nine habits of healthy breathing, the foundation of good mental and physical health. While you develop these habits, you will learn simple strategies to quickly relieve acute anxiety symptoms, abort a panic attack, stay calm under pressure, and switch off at night to enjoy quiet, restful sleep. You will read about lives transformed just by learning to breathe properly. You will be delighted at how easy making these changes can be. You will be shown how to blend better breathing practice into your everyday life.

Deep breathing myth

You may be more than a little surprised to learn that good breathing is the opposite of what you think!

Have you ever heard that it is best to breathe in (and out) a lot of air, deeply, fully and even forcefully? In with the good air, out with the bad, right? If you think this is good for you, you are not alone. But you need to think again. Ironically, it is a recipe for feeling anxious, spaced out, light-headed, and for provoking a panic attack.

Perfect for the time-poor and the overwhelmed

The wonderful thing about changing your breathing is that you have around 16,000 opportunities a day to make a difference. You don't have to stop other parts of your life. You don't need equipment or special positions. You simply need to be more mindful about your breathing so that change is possible and natural.

The suggestions make it manageable for even the most stressed, overwhelmed and deflated of people. Before the end of Chapter 5 you will be on your way to breathing better and feeling better. Some change is generally apparent within hours, even minutes. This is an opportunity to empower yourself and improve your health and the quality of your life. Like so many before you, you may even get your old life back – the one you thought was gone forever.

ACTION STEPS

Having done your breathing quiz, it is helpful to watch yourself some more. Most people start to notice things that they hadn't before. For example, they do a lot more mouth breathing than they thought. Asking someone else what they have noticed about your breathing can be helpful.

- Continue to watch your breathing.
- Have you caught yourself with your mouth open?
- Ask someone if they hear your breathing when you're asleep or awake.
- Has anyone noticed that you sigh a lot?
- How many times a day do you yawn?
- Go back and adjust your scoring on page 6 if needed.

Don't try and change anything yet – just observe. We will get to the changes soon.

CHAPTER 2

Anxiety and stress disorders – what are they?

This chapter explains what anxiety is and discusses different types of anxiety and stress-related disorders. It also looks at some different management and treatment approaches.

Note: The purpose of this chapter is to give some background on anxiety disorders, not to classify you according to a particular disorder. It is also important not to self-diagnose. If you have not been diagnosed and think you may be experiencing any of these disorders, see your doctor.

WHAT IS ANXIETY?

Anxiety is a feeling of worry, nervousness, fear, or apprehension. We all experience anxiety at one time or another, the shaky knees, the thudding heart, the racing mind. It is a normal human experience to feel fear. In fact, it is an important emotion – it keeps us safe at times of danger. Without anxiety you might walk down dark alleys by yourself at night or pick fights with people four times your size. It's a protective mechanism, and it's automatic, but it loses its ability to warn you of danger if it's on all the time.

Unfortunately, many people feel anxious all the time, or experience anxiety even when no immediate danger is present. It never goes away. You are stuck in the fight-or-flight state. Anxiety ranges from a mild feeling of unease to extreme fear. It affects how you feel and behave on a daily basis and it can also manifest in real physical symptoms that can be very uncomfortable and even frightening. You may feel helpless because of these mental and physical symptoms you wrestle with every day. Your edginess, obsessive thoughts, racing heart, dizziness, and trembling in response to 'stressors', threaten to take over your life.

Of the dozens of mental and physical symptoms (see Chapter 3) that can occur, many are directly connected to dysfunctional breathing, and they can be improved through breathing retraining. Correct breathing is the off-switch for the fight-or-flight stress response.

When anxiety is debilitating and chronic it may be diagnosed as an *anxiety disorder.*

ANXIETY DISORDERS

Anxiety disorders are the most common psychological conditions or 'mental health disorders' in the developed world. There are five major anxiety disorders.

Generalised anxiety disorder

Generalised anxiety disorder is persistent, excessive and often irrational anxiety and fear about everyday things such as finances, family problems or illness or situations that may never happen. Those who suffer with this disorder often find themselves worrying all the time; they can't turn their mind off from worried thinking. They never 'feel normal'. Generalised anxiety disorder is said to be the most common mental illness in Australia, affecting approximately five per cent of people at some time in their lives.

Panic attacks and panic disorder

A panic attack is an intense feeling of anxiety or fearfulness that comes on suddenly. It usually lasts only a few minutes, but in some cases may return in waves for an hour or two. Panic attacks are often associated with feelings of dread, that something bad is going to happen, and physical symptoms that can be so intense that some people become hospitalised fearing that something is dangerously wrong with their health. For example, with a severe panic attack people may feel they are having a heart attack, going to die or going insane (and yet they are not). Experiencing a panic attack may be one of the most intensely frightening and uncomfortable experiences of a person's life.

Panic attacks can be triggered by anxiety or stress, or they can be related to a specific situation, for example driving a car over a high bridge, or they can appear 'out of the blue' and be seemingly unrelated to any particular situation. You are said to have *panic disorder* if you become chronically fearful about having another panic attack, or if you have a panic attack at least four times a month. About three out of ten people experience at least one panic attack in their life. Around three per cent of the population has a panic disorder.

Phobias

When a person has a phobia, they have an irrational fear of things, for example spiders or fish, or fear a particular situation. Examples are social situations (social phobia), unfamiliar places or big shopping centres (agoraphobia), or small enclosed spaces such as lifts (claustrophobia).

Some degree of social anxiety is normal, such as discomfort while public speaking, but when the fear of social situations is intense it can severely disrupt your life. Then there are so many things you can no longer do, like attend work functions and big family celebrations. Your world becomes compressed. Some people with agoraphobia may never leave their home.

Approximately nine per cent of people experience a phobia at some time in their lives. Phobias are twice as common in women as in men. It is fairly common for people with agoraphobia to also have panic disorder.

Obsessive-compulsive disorder

This is experiencing excessive or unwanted thoughts (obsessions) that cause anxiety and make people feel they need to carry out certain rituals or repetitive behaviours (compulsions) in order to feel less anxious. An example of an obsession is constantly worrying about developing an infectious disease, while a compulsion is feeling anxious if you do not wash your hands repeatedly throughout the day. Obsessive compulsive disorder (OCD) affects approximately two to three per cent of people at some time in their lives.

Post-traumatic stress disorder

A person with post-traumatic stress disorder may experience anxiety or panic attacks following an event that threatened their life or safety or that of others around them. This can be a major car or other accident, war, physical violence, sexual assault, or natural disasters such as bushfires or floods. A major feature of post-traumatic stress disorder is reliving the traumatic event through dreams, nightmares or flashbacks. While it is normal for someone who has experienced a traumatic event to relive the event in order to process it, it is a problem when reliving the event causes a significant disruption to their daily life. Around eight per cent of the population are said to be affected by post-traumatic stress disorder at some time in their lives.

DEPRESSION

Depression is a mood disorder rather than an anxiety disorder. It is a serious illness, more than just a low mood that anyone may feel occasionally. It is an intense experience of sadness, like a thick lead blanket of despair weighing you down. Depression may be temporary or a long-term disorder. With depression, you may find it difficult to function day to day. You may experience loss of sleep and appetite, and loss of interest and pleasure in previously enjoyable activities, making you withdraw from others. Depression affects as much as 10 per cent of the population. While depression and anxiety are distinct syndromes, they co-occur in around half of all cases. It is now thought that many people develop depression as a result of living with anxiety.

YOU ARE NOT ALONE!

It's no exaggeration to say there is an epidemic of anxiety and it's a global problem.

In Australia, an estimated 14 per cent of adults experience some type of anxiety disorder in a year. This is around one in six women and one in ten men. One in four people will experience an anxiety disorder at some stage in their lifetime.[2.1] Between 2000 and 2011, antidepressant use nearly doubled in Australia.[2.2]

In the United States of America, an estimated 57 million adults have an anxiety disorder, and two thirds of these are women.[2.3] When you combine anxiety disorders and depression, some estimates put the number of people affected to be as high as 18 per cent, more than one in six people. In the United Kingdom, National Health Service hospital appointments for anxiety quadrupled between 2007 and 2011. In 2001, the World Health Organization's Director General, Dr Gro Harlem, said that major depression was the leading cause of disability globally.[2.4]

High rates of anxiety disorders have also been reported in children and youth. In the 16–24 age group, it is estimated they affect one in five females and almost one in ten males.[2.3] About half of people with anxiety disorders experience their first symptoms by the age of 11.[2.5]

SOCIAL REPERCUSSIONS

If an anxiety disorder is not addressed, the symptoms of anxiety can start to take over your life. They can affect relationships, make it difficult to hold down a job and lead to substance abuse. Partners of anxiety sufferers may also suffer health effects if their sleep is disturbed due to your sleep problems, or if they worry about you.

STRESS-RELATED DISORDERS

Stress is a state of bodily, mental or emotional tension caused by problems in your life or work that threaten to overwhelm your capacity to cope or adapt. It can cause strong feelings of worry or anxiety. Stress is highly subjective – one person's fun may be another person's stressor. Long-term anxiety itself is a significant stress on your body.

Chronic stress can provoke physiological changes in the body. Medical conditions believed to be related to stress include high blood pressure, mouth ulcers, various skin conditions, cold sores, digestive disorders, headaches, and insomnia to name a few.

ANXIETY AND PHYSICAL ILLNESS

Chronic anxiety has been linked to a higher incidence of and poorer recovery from respiratory disorders,[2.6; 2.7] hypertension, heart disease,[2.8] and gastrointestinal disorders. A 2007 New Zealand study of subjects with gastroenteritis (inflammation of the digestive tract) found an association between high anxiety levels and the development of irritable bowel syndrome following a bowel infection.[2.9] Depression has also been linked with irritable bowel syndrome.[2.10]

THE BREATHING CONNECTION

You will understand why these conditions are related to chronic stress and anxiety once you understand the breathing connection. Most importantly, you will have hope for better all-round health and wellbeing. Improving your breathing improves many body functions.

TREATMENT APPROACHES TO ANXIETY DISORDERS

This section gives an overview of different treatment and management options available for anxiety disorders and depression. It's not a complete summary of all that is on offer.

Psychological treatments (talking therapies)

For anxiety linked to chronic negative thinking or emotional stress, or when triggered by a traumatic event or high-stress situation, your doctor may suggest counselling. Sometimes this is called 'talk therapy'. These aim to address the psychological factors and behaviours behind anxiety and mood disorders. They help you to understand your anxiety triggers, challenge faulty thinking patterns and give you skills to deal with stress situations more effectively. The better known forms of psychological therapy are psychotherapy, counselling, mindfulness, and cognitive behaviour therapy.

In times gone by, caring family members gathered around a depressed relative and gave them support, care, reassurance, and a listening ear. Today, in our hectic world we have less time and are often separated by great distances from family members. Mental health professionals in the public health or private sectors conduct this important work.

Nutritional approach

Nutrient deficiencies, digestive disorders and conditions such as hypoglycaemia and insulin resistance often play a part in anxiety and mood disorders.[2.12] There is also evidence that the modern diet, particularly refined sugars, may contribute to anxiety. By making better food choices and taking supplements, you may reduce the need for medications. Chapter 9 gives information about the food-breathing connection.

Medication

The most common treatment for anxiety and mood disorders is medication – anti-anxiety and antidepressant drugs. Medications may be prescribed alone or with psychological therapies. Drugs have the advantage of often working quickly (faster than nutritional and psychological treatment), so drug therapy will always be an essential part of medicine. However, the results are not always positive or permanent. There may also be troubling side-effects and possible dependency.

Doctors all over the world prescribe antidepressants more than almost any other drug, but the debate over their effectiveness rages on. In some countries, prescriptions have more than doubled in a decade. Around one in ten European adults take antidepressants.

While experts agree that antidepressant and anti-anxiety medications can be effective for short-term mental distress, and to help people get through immensely difficult situations like trauma or bereavement, much research shows that anxiety is more successfully treated with cognitive behaviour therapy (see Glossary). Psychotherapy alone or with medication appears to be more effective than medication alone in the treatment of anxiety and depression.

Note: Do not reduce or go off any prescribed medication without your doctor's recommendation and supervision. Do not use this book as a substitute for professional help.

Lifestyle approaches

Your doctor may suggest lifestyle approaches, such as reducing coffee and alcohol, regular physical exercise, massage, relaxation classes, meditation, yoga, or a holiday.

Breathing retraining

Breathing retraining, the approach offered in this book, is a *functional* or *physiological* therapy and is science-based. It identifies and addresses the *dysfunctional* breathing habits that often underlie anxiety disorders, destabilising blood and brain chemistry, and interfering with body functions, including the nervous system.

It's a self-management tool. You learn how to control your breathing to relieve acute symptoms. You learn how to correct your baseline, everyday breathing pattern to prevent symptoms and support long-term physical and mental wellbeing. You learn to breathe correctly at rest, when under stress and during sleep and exercise.

You usually get immediate relief from acute symptoms – you feel calmer, your heartbeat slows down – and you notice broad positive changes within days as your correct breathing replaces faulty breathing habits. You can use breathing retraining simultaneously with drug, psychological or behavioural therapy because it does not interfere with them. In fact, it can enhance their benefits.

Despite its safety, scientific validity and appropriateness, breathing retraining has not received the same attention as pharmaceutical and psychological therapies.

PSYCHOLOGY AND BREATHING TECHNIQUES

Although psychologists generally recognise the link between breathing and anxiety symptoms, and may teach *breathing techniques* as part of a therapy session, this is different and not nearly as comprehensive an approach as *breathing retraining.*

Breathing retraining is also vastly different from the breathing techniques commonly taught in yoga, fitness and Pilates classes. More on this in Chapter 10.

YES, THERE IS HOPE

When you suffer from anxiety and depression, you feel as though you can't get relief, because that's how these disorders make you feel. But you can recover.

To find an effective treatment for any health disorder, you first need to identify any underlying conditions or dysfunctions, and then choose an approach, or approaches to directly address them. That's what this book is about. It helps you to:

- identify physiologically abnormal breathing patterns that cause biochemical mayhem and fuel the body's stress response, and then
- use breathing retraining to address them.

Scores of studies have confirmed the link. I've been helping clients for 23 years to correct their breathing. I've had thousands of people tell me or write to me of their success.

Before we get into it, we'll look in the next chapter at how your body reacts – the symptoms you experience – when you have an anxiety disorder. This is important to know.

CHAPTER 3

Signs, symptoms, causes of anxiety disorders

This chapter outlines the typical psychological and physical signs and symptoms people with anxiety disorders experience. You get a chance to identify and rate yours on a *symptom tracker*. Later, you will use this to reassess your symptoms as your breathing improves.

HOW DOES ANXIETY LOOK?

Observe: do you have a heaving chest, are your shoulders up, is your mouth open, do you take big gasping breaths?

Or do you look cool, calm and collected on the outside, but like a duck, you're paddling like crazy under the water?

HOW DOES ANXIETY FEEL?

The most common symptoms are racing thoughts, constant worrying and irrational fears, and continual feelings of stress, inner tension, edginess, and a sense of impending doom. You might also have feelings of detachment, unreality, being 'spaced out', or have a sense of not being in control. You may have trouble thinking and reasoning; decision-making can seem ridiculously stressful and laboured. This in turn increases stress levels; you are on a roundabout that you can't get off. You may wake irritable and unhappy.

Anxiety is a lot more than just the in-your-head stuff. There are often also physical symptoms: dry mouth, palpitating heart, quickened breathing, dripping armpits, trembling legs, the feeling of a vice or tight band around your head or chest. You can go to bed to 'escape' but lie awake for hours, tossing and turning all night. You can wake feeling more tired than when you went to bed. Living with constant anxiety is a hard gig.

FIGURE 3.1: ANXIETY: MIND AND BODY SYMPTOMS

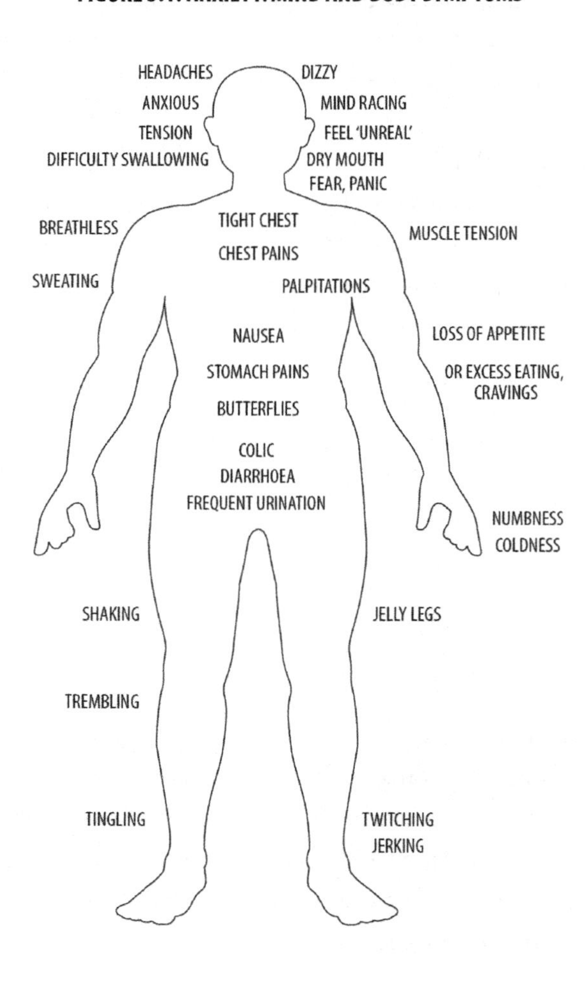

HOW DOES A PANIC ATTACK FEEL?

Panic attacks often involve mental distress, fear of losing control, fear of going crazy or passing out, feelings of doom, and severe anxiety about health. However, they are most well-known for the physical symptoms that accompany them and which often appear before the mental symptoms. The physical symptoms are similar to those for anxiety and can be more intense.

- What *psychological* symptoms do you notice when you are anxious?

- What *physical* symptoms do you notice when you are anxious?

- What happens to you during a panic attack?

HOW ARE YOU DIAGNOSED WITH AN ANXIETY DISORDER?

Until fairly recently, most people weren't officially diagnosed for their anxiety disorder. They may have been (unhelpfully) told to "get over it", "move on", "get a grip on yourself" or "stop being a drama queen". Now, anxiety is generally treated with more respect and concern.

The family doctor usually makes the first diagnosis, based on your symptoms and responses to questions. Your doctor might also do a physical check to see if something other than anxiety is the reason for your problems. They might look for a thyroid disorder, or do an electrocardiogram (ECG) if you have experienced heart issues. They will want to rule out anxiety or depression that may be associated with another mental illness such as bipolar disorder.

In trying to identify a cause of anxiety or mental illness, the doctor may consider genetic, biological, environmental, psychological, and physiological factors. Despite the monstrous size of the issue and considerable research over several decades, there is no firm medical understanding of what causes anxiety or mood disorders, and there are no standard laboratory tests to diagnose them.

FINDING THE CAUSE

Brain chemistry imbalance or not?

A current hypothesis is that an imbalance in brain chemicals causes mental illness. But it is a hypothesis only, and it is under debate. No direct links have been discovered between our brain chemistry and anxiety and depression.

To affirm that brain chemistry is unbalanced, you have to be able to measure it. According to internationally known psychiatrist Dr Peter Breggin, "There are no known biochemical imbalances and no tests for them. That's why psychiatrists do not draw blood or perform spinal taps to determine the presence of a biochemical imbalance in patients."[3.1]

What is known?

There are several neurotransmitters in the brain that affect mood and emotion.

A *neurotransmitter* is a naturally occurring chemical substance that allows 'messages' to be carried along nerve pathways. Two examples are serotonin and dopamine.

However, scientists studying depression are unsure exactly how they work, and there are no techniques for measuring the actual levels of neurotransmitters in the synapses (spaces) between nerve cells in the brain. No scientific evidence can currently show serotonin deficiency as a cause of any mental disorder.[3.2]

Psychologists focus on the cognitive and emotional indicators of inner conflict or negative feelings. They may seek to identify a precipitating traumatic experience such as the death of a close relative, divorce, serious illness, or other unpleasant emotional experiences. The mind, brain and body are connected; what occurs in one, affects the other.

It is rare to assess a person's baseline breathing pattern, and this would be a very valuable addition to current diagnostic practice. A disturbance in the normal rhythm, rate and volume of breathing influences blood and cell chemistry, the production of stress hormones and neurotransmitters, the oxygenation of the brain (and everywhere else), and how your nervous system (and almost every other system) functions. Unlike the shaky hypothesis that people with anxiety disorders have abnormal brain chemistry, it is scientific law that physiology and blood and brain chemistry are altered in people with disordered breathing.

ASSESS YOUR SYMPTOMS

You may be surprised to learn how many of the physical and psychological symptoms of dysfunctional breathing are also common symptoms in anxiety and panic disorders. The symptoms listed in Table 3.1 below are divided into the different body systems they relate to. Please take the time to fill it in now.

Instructions for completing Table 3.1

Write today's date at the top of the Assessment 1 column of Table 3.1. Put an 'x' in the My Symptoms column next to the symptoms you experience at least once a week.

Now rate each marked symptom in the Assessment 1 column using the tick scoring system below.

SCORING SYSTEM FOR SYMPTOM FREQUENCY

No tick	Never
✓	Sometimes
✓ ✓	Often
✓ ✓ ✓	Always
✓ ✓ ✓ ✓	Always and intense

Symptom Score = total number of ticks

Add up the number of ticks in the Assessment 1 column and record the result in the space at the bottom of Table 3.1. This gives you a Symptom Score.

TABLE 3.1: DYSFUNCTIONAL BREATHING SYMPTOM TRACKER

MY SYMPTOMS	SYMPTOMS	ASSESSMENT 1 Date:	ASSESSMENT 2 Date:	ASSESSMENT 3 Date:
	PSYCHOLOGICAL			
	Anxiety, apprehension, worry, fear			
	Tension, revved up, jittery, jumpy, restless			
	Panic attacks			
	'Spaced out', sense of unreality, or like 'losing my mind'			
	Poor concentration or memory			
	NEUROLOGICAL			
	Feeling dizzy or unsteady; faintness			
	Numbness or tingling sensations			
	Hot flushes or chills; cold face, fingers, feet			
	Trembling, shaking, weakness in limbs			
	Muscle tension, pain, spasm, cramping			
	Headache			
	RESPIRATORY			
	Rapid, heavy or laboured breathing			
	Short of breath resting, talking			
	Easily breathless with exertion			
	Chest tightness			
	Inability to take a deep breath			
	Dry cough, throat tickle, throat clearing			
	Sighing, extra-deep breaths			
	Frequent yawning or when not tired			
	Runny nose			
	Choking or smothering feelings			

MY SYMPTOMS	SYMPTOMS	ASSESSMENT 1 Date:	ASSESSMENT 2 Date:	ASSESSMENT 3 Date:
	Snoring, snorting or gasping during sleep			
	CARDIOVASCULAR			
	Irregular, pounding or racing heart			
	Chest discomfort unrelated to heart			
	DIGESTIVE			
	Nausea, diarrhoea, colic			
	Dry mouth; difficulty swallowing			
	Heartburn, belching, flatulence			
	GENERAL OR OVERLAPPING			
	Sweating, clamminess			
	Frequent or urgent urination			
	Restless, interrupted sleep; insomnia			
	Toilet visits overnight			
	Frightening or vivid dreams			
	Waking tired			
	Tiredness, low energy, 'drained'			
	Exercise intolerant, lack of stamina			
	⇦ NUMBER OF SYMPTOMS TOTAL SYMPTOM SCORE ⇨			

How many different symptoms do you have? [ ]

What's your total Symptom Score? [ ]

Many of my clients mark off more than half; some tick them all. A symptom score over 60 is common. This list is adapted from Fried[3.3] and Laffey[3.4].

I suggest you use a bookmark in this page so you can find it easily when we refer back to it.

'THE CRYING LIST'

Don't worry if you get emotional completing this – you won't be the first! Quite a few of my clients have cried on their first visit as a reaction to realising that the symptoms they have been suffering, often for decades, may be connected to breathing incorrectly, which up until now has been missed. Tears of distress and frustration can transform into tears of joy and hope knowing that there is a way out.

Sheldon had all these symptoms, many of them severe, along with his diagnoses of general anxiety disorder, social phobia, depression, and hypertension. His initial symptom score was 111. It had dropped to 58 within 24 hours of his first breathing retraining consultation. At his fourth session, he said that his social anxiety of 10 years standing had "gone away".

Note: The Dysfunctional Breathing Symptom Tracker is a screening tool to help you determine whether you might have dysfunctional breathing. It is not designed or intended to make a diagnosis of an anxiety disorder (or sleep disorder) or to take the place of professional diagnosis or consultation.

ACTION STEPS

- Observe what is going on in your body over the next day or two.
- Come back and review the Dysfunctional Breathing Symptom Tracker.
- Adjust your scoring if needed.

Many people find they have more symptoms than they realised because they had accepted them as normal!

How often do you sigh? How poor is your concentration?

Monitor your sleep for a few nights: how many toilet trips do you make? How do you feel when you wake up? Is your mouth dry? Do you have a headache?

CHAPTER 4

How does your breathing compare to normal?

How should you breathe? How does a calm, relaxed, focused person breathe? How does a silent, restful sleeper breathe?

How does a wired, spaced-out, distraught, overwhelmed worrier breathe?

Most importantly, how do you breathe?

Most of us are familiar with the normal, healthy range for our temperature, heart rate, blood pressure, and blood sugar and these are measured as a routine part of any health check. 'Breathing norms' by contrast are often overlooked.

What you may not realise is that your breathing does not just go berserk when you 'go off the deep end' or have a panic attack. Nor if you are a heavy snorer does your breathing go crazy during sleep before returning to a perfectly normal pattern when you wake. The way you are breathing right now, your *baseline breathing pattern*, could be priming you for a meltdown at work or a noisy and restless night.

ASSESSING YOUR BASELINE BREATHING PATTERN

Back in Chapter 1, you filled in the breathing quiz: Table 1.1: Breathing Pattern Self-Assessment. This involved some simple observations to determine if your *baseline breathing pattern* was normal or not.

You checked the

- feel of your breathing – easy or restricted and unsatisfying
- rhythm of your breathing – smooth and regular, or erratic and with lots of yawns or sighs
- sound of your breathing – silent or audible
- route of your breathing – nose or mouth

- dominant location of your breathing –diaphragm or upper chest
- rate of your breathing – slow or fast
- how obvious or heavy your breathing (an indicator of volume)

In this chapter we will compare your results to what is *physiologically normal* baseline breathing. Then you will know what needs changing.

BREATHING BASICS

A big part of the success of breathing retraining is that people really 'get it'. They get what they've been doing wrong breathing-wise, and they get how that can lead to the worrying and debilitating symptoms they suffer from. A basic understanding of how breathing works helps with this, and that's what we're going to get into now. If you want more technical information, please refer to the list of physiology texts provided in the Chapter References and Resource Materials on page 195.

Oxygen and carbon dioxide in balance

When you breathe, air moves into and out of the body. The main purpose of the breathing process is to bring about the exchange of two gases – oxygen and carbon dioxide – and to maintain them at very particular levels for the body to function best. Both these gases are critical for life.

Oxygen makes up 20 per cent of the air you breathe in. You inhale it into your lungs, into the alveoli – the small air sacs where gases are exchanged. The oxygen then passes into your bloodstream. It attaches itself to the red blood cells (haemoglobin) and then is taken by the bloodstream to your organs and tissues. The haemoglobin then releases the oxygen, which moves into your cells where it is used as fuel to 'burn' or oxidise fats and carbohydrates, making energy to drive your body.

The main by-products of this energy production are carbon dioxide and water. The carbon dioxide moves out of the cells and into the blood. The bloodstream takes the carbon dioxide to your lungs where some (what is not needed) can be breathed out. Compared to what you breathe in, there is a lot more carbon dioxide in your blood, in your lungs and in the air that you breathe out. Only a tiny amount (0.038 per cent) of the air you breathe in is carbon dioxide. Yet the ideal level of carbon dioxide to have in the air sacs in your lungs is 5.5–6.5 per cent.

Your body makes carbon dioxide and in effect concentrates it in your blood and lungs. You exhale not to get rid of carbon dioxide, but to maintain it at the optimal level. Too much or too little is a problem. Therefore, breathing too little or too much is also a problem.

WHAT DOES NORMAL BREATHING LOOK LIKE?

This is how normal breathing is:

- **Comfortable:** easy and satisfying.
- **Regular:** smooth, rhythmic, with even timing, even-sized breaths both awake and asleep.
- **Silent:** during the day, at night, and with light activity and light exercise.
- **Nasal**: coming in and going out through the nose, all day and all night and even with exercise. The nose is quite capable of supplying enough air for a well-trained, good-breathing person to run a marathon (Yes! That is not a misprint).
- **Diaphragmatic**: movement occurs mainly at the level of the diaphragm (solar plexus); there is minimal (if any) movement of the upper chest, shoulders or lower belly.
- **8–12 breaths per minute (adults).** It is higher in children.
- **Tidal Volume 500 ml**: *tidal volume* is the amount of air breathed in and out in one breath. At rest and during sleep, normal tidal volume is around 500 ml. It will be more with exercise.
- **Minute Volume 4–6 litres**: *minute volume* is the total volume of air breathed in and out of your lungs in a minute. At rest, normal is between four and six litres. It will be more with exercise. A person breathing 10 breaths per minute at rest, with each breath being 500 ml, has a minute volume of five litres per minute.

Normal volume breathing

This is a critical element of normal breathing. You yourself cannot accurately measure the volume you breathe in one breath or each minute. The equipment to do so is usually only in hospitals. However, you can get a fair indication by considering the following.

An ideal 500 ml size breath will be silent and gentle and almost invisible, with just a small outward movement of the solar plexus area occurring as you breathe in. See Figure 4.1.Your nostrils won't flare. You won't gulp in through your mouth. You're not embarrassed by the noise of your breathing when at the cinema. Your bed partner does not complain about annoying noise or air gushing over them at night. You won't take more than 14 breaths in a minute.

FIGURE 4.1 SOLAR PLEXUS

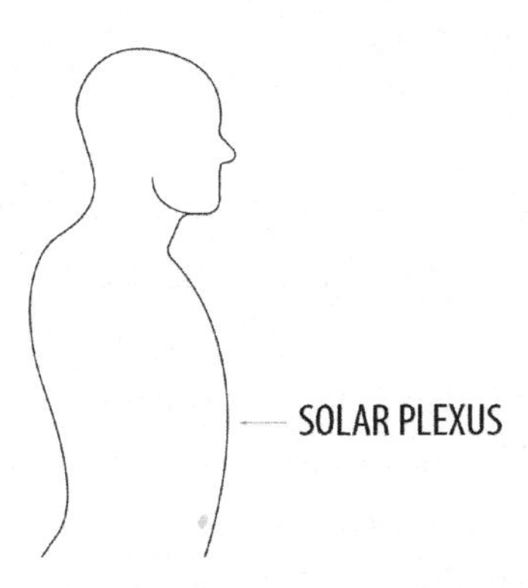

At rest and during sleep, passing 4–6 litres of air per minute through your lungs supplies more than enough oxygen to load up your red blood cells with oxygen and keeps carbon dioxide levels in your lungs and blood within the optimal range.

FIGURE 4.2 NORMAL BREATHING

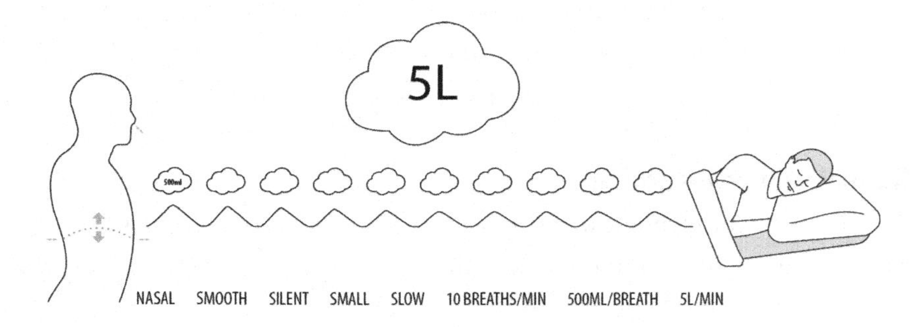

During exercise, more carbon dioxide is produced and more oxygen is needed. A healthy breather naturally breathes faster and deeper during exercise. Less oxygen is needed during most stages of sleep, and the healthy breather naturally breathes less while asleep, and is very quiet and peaceful.

WHAT DOES POOR BREATHING LOOKS LIKE?

- **Uncomfortable**, heavy, restricted or unsatisfying.
- **Irregular** or unstable: varying breath sizes and timing, yawning, sighing, throat clearing, extra deep breaths, breath holding during the day; erratic, snoring, snorting, gasping, breath holding/sleep apnoea during sleep).
- **Upper Chest**: upper chest moves noticeably, rib muscles used more as well as accessory (shoulder and neck area) breathing muscles.
- **Mouth Breathing**: always or sometimes; common when feeling stressed or moving about.
- **Fast**: 14 or more breaths per minute; 18–22 is not uncommon for anxiety sufferers (this is their baseline when they are relatively calm).
- **High Tidal Volume**: big breaths fill lungs too much; overly empty lungs when exhaling. Sighs can be three times a normal tidal volume, and may occur 4–25 times in a 15-minute period with anxiety patients. [4.1]
- **High Minute Volume**: average 12 litres per minute shown in anxiety sufferers. [4.2]

Research shows greater instability in respiratory rate, minute volume and carbon dioxide levels in anxiety and panic patients compared to normal 'control' subjects. The greatest instability is seen in people with a panic disorder. [4.3]

Figure 4.3 shows what disordered breathing can look like.

FIGURE 4.3: DISORDERED BREATHING

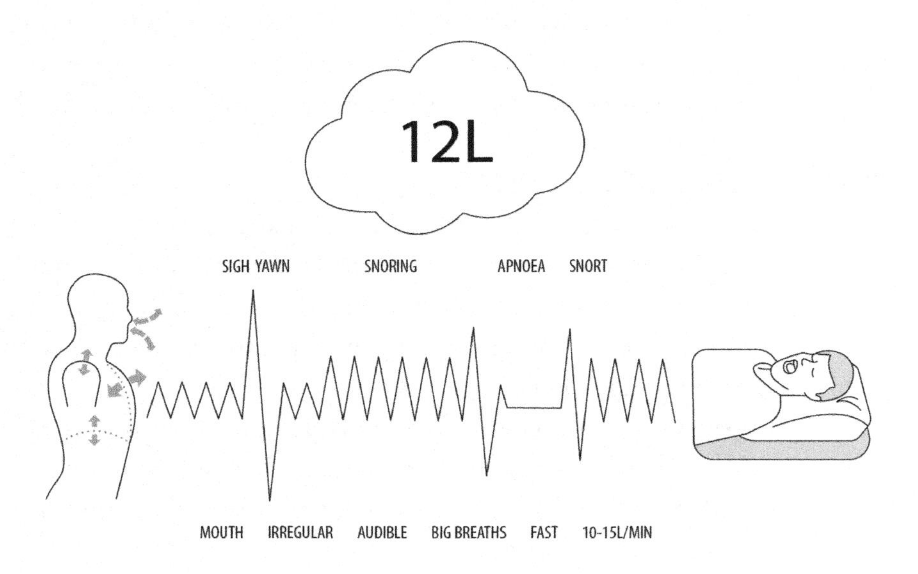

TABLE 4.1: NORMAL VS OVER-BREATHING – AT REST

PARAMETER	NORMAL	OVER-BREATHING
Rhythm	Regular, smooth	Irregular, sighs, yawns
Sound	Silent	Audible
Route	Nose	Mouth
Location (predominant)	Diaphragm	Upper chest
Respiration rate	8–12	14+
Tidal volume	500 ml	> 600 ml
Minute volume	4–6 litres	> 7 litres

HOW DO YOU COMPARE WITH NORMAL?

Compare the results from your breathing assessment (Table 1.1) on page 6 to the norms in Table 4.1. If normal, healthy breathing is nasal, smooth, silent, small, soft, slow, satisfying, and relatively still, how do you compare?

If you are like the thousands of people with asthma, anxiety and sleep disorders who I have helped, you will have discovered that you do not breathe correctly, either during the day or at night, and that you generally or at least sometimes breathe too much. You *over-breathe.*

OVER-BREATHING/HYPERVENTILATION

The terms *hyperventilation* and *over-breathing* are generally interchangeable. I mainly use the term *over-breathing* as most people think of hyperventilation with the obvious rapid breathing that occurs during a stressful event or with a panic attack. This is easy to see, but chronic hyperventilation/over-breathing is far more common and subtler and so it often goes unrecognised. Its causes can be prolonged exposure to stressors or bad habits. Anything that stresses your body increases your breathing. The stressor may be psychological, e.g. grief, job loss; physical, e.g. slumped posture, extreme exercise, heat wave; environmental, e.g. pollens, pollution; or biological, e.g. bacterial infection. The causes or triggers of over-breathing will be discussed further in Chapter 8.

Over-breathing means breathing more than normal; more than what is needed to fuel your current level of activity. If you are sleeping, or sitting reading this book, you only need around five litres of air each minute – about 10 breaths of 500 ml each. Taking 20 breaths of 600 ml, or 14 of 850 ml, gives you 12 litres of air consumption in a minute. This is significant over-breathing, but is likely to go unnoticed. Throw in one 2000-ml sigh and you are near 14 litres a minute. Frequent sighing is one of the classic indicators of an anxiety disorder.

The tidal volume in sighs, yawns, long drawn-out breaths, coughs and snores is invariably larger than 500 ml. Research suggests a typical sigh is around 1,600–2,000 ml and can be as high as 3,000 ml – that's three litres! Frequent sighing is a sign of a body under stress. I have seen sighing disappear very quickly through breathing retraining.

The other ways of over-breathing are mouth breathing and fast breathing.

The accessory breathing muscles – shoulder and neck area– are meant to be on standby for when you need extra lung capacity for intense exercise, and in situations of fear or threat. They are not meant to be so involved in normal resting breathing. They are muscles of 'desperation' rather than 'inspiration'.

Upper-chest breathing is far less efficient than diaphragm breathing and it seriously disadvantages you. The muscles tire easily and produce lactic acid, which is the reason why many people experience sore chest muscles after a panic or asthma attack. It's also why after a night of heavy snoring, a snorer can wake with their chest feeling sore and bruised.

And you thought it was from being over-zealously prodded by a sleep-deprived partner!

Mouth breathing is so common that few people notice it. It is more common when you are stressed. When you breathe in through your mouth, the tidal volumes are larger than normal and the air rushes in faster. The mouth after all is a much bigger opening than the two nostrils.

The bottom line is that your average anxiety sufferer has an abnormal breathing pattern. Characteristically they over-breathe all the time, not just when they're having an anxiety attack. It just becomes greater and more obvious then. My observations of thousands of clients with anxiety disorders suggest they have excessive minute volumes even when they are nose breathing.

Are you over-breathing?

How many of these signs apply to you? Tick them off in Table 4.2 below.

TABLE 4.2: TYPICAL SIGNS OF OVER-BREATHING

Signs of over-breathing	Tick for yes
Breathing through the mouth	
Heavy nose breathing	
Audible breathing awake and/or asleep	
Fast breathing (over 14 breaths a minute)	
Upper-chest movement	
Shoulder movement with breathing	
Irregular/erratic breathing	
Frequent sighs	
Excessive yawning	
Snoring	

When over-breathing becomes a habit, the symptoms you feel may be spread across several body systems – like those in Table 3.1.

With acute hyperventilation:

- breathing speeds up
- heart races

- adrenaline pours into bloodstream
- muscles tense up.

Note: It is also important to know that hyperventilation may be caused by a medical condition other than anxiety. Also, some symptoms of hyperventilation may be associated with other ailments and disorders. Your doctor can determine this for you.

Does all this surprise you? Did you think that breathing lots of air was good for you? This common belief may well qualify as public health enemy number one.

WHY IS OVER-BREATHING BAD FOR YOU?

Having the odd breath here and there out of balance is not a problem. But when most of the 20,000–30,000 breaths you take in a day are big breaths, the cumulative effect on your body function is significant. You would expect consistently high blood-sugar levels, high blood pressure or a heart rate twice the norm to cause a problem or two, and breathing at double or triple the normal rate also causes problems.

Over-breathing is associated with many symptoms in any organ or system of the body. It can dehydrate, irritate and inflame the tissues lining the nose, sinuses, throat, and lungs; it can alter your blood chemistry and rev up your nervous system. The repercussions are felt in the psyche, and respiratory, cardiovascular, neurological, and digestive systems. These effects are covered in more detail in the next chapter.

Chronic over-breathing often holds the explanation for a wide range of health problems.

NOSE, MOUTH, SIGH – VOLUME COMPARISON

To compare the tidal volume of air used for nose- and mouth breathing and when you sigh, try the following:

1. Place one hand on the upper chest and the other on the solar plexus. Note where and how much movement you feel when you nose breathe.
2. Keeping your hands in place, now open your mouth and breathe through it. Did you notice an increase in the amount of movement, indicating a larger tidal volume?
3. Keep your hands in place and now sigh. Did you feel the upper chest heave?

OVER-BREATHING IS OVERLOOKED

Medical scientist and physician, Professor Konstantin Buteyko, coined the term 'hidden hyperventilation' because chronic hyperventilation is often very subtle. His exhaustive research in Russia, spanning several decades from the 1950s, showed that chronic hyperventilation was very common in the general population and that it was a factor in the development of chronic diseases.[4.4]

Chest physician, Dr Claude Lum, published extensively on the hyperventilation syndrome. In his article, *Hyperventilation: the tip of the iceberg* (1975), he had this to say.

> The many organs involved are often reflected in the number of specialists to whom the patient gets referred, and my colleagues have variously dubbed this the "multiple doctor" or the "fat folder syndrome". Indeed, the thickness of the case file is often an important diagnostic clue.[4.5]

At different times, Jane was convinced she had MS, a stroke or a heart problem. She'd had all the tests – EEG, ECG, stress test, nerve conduction tests, sleep study. Jane didn't make the connection with her breathing, and neither did her GP, heart specialist or neurologist. She felt she was "breaking down and going mad". When I first saw Jane, she had 70 symptoms on the hyperventilation syndrome list and that went down to 49 after just one lesson. Her total symptom score was 40 per cent less the next day.

Do you identify with Jane?

KNOWLEDGE IS POWER

Are you starting to see how over-breathing could be behind many of the symptoms you have been suffering? In Chapter 6, we explore these connections. But rest assured, there is a way out of this. You can change the way you breathe and like Jane, it usually doesn't take long before you begin to feel better. First you recognise your poor breathing habits, then you undo them, and then you get back to normal breathing and enjoy the benefits. Go to the next page now and learn your first exercise and be on your way.

CHAPTER 5

Let's begin

...if you haven't already.

With what you now know, I'm sure you'll want to start making some changes. Here is some guidance to do just that, before we get to the breathing program itself in Part Two.

Because changing your breathing can be very powerful, it is especially important if you have anxiety to make adjustments slowly, otherwise the changes can be too fast for comfort. Make small, manageable changes and blend them into your normal day. You will gradually undo poor breathing habits and replace them with good ones for the long term. Making changes shouldn't be hard, time-consuming or scary. You will be surprised how quickly you feel better even with small changes, as with the Cloud Exercise below.

THE CLOUD CONCEPT

We start with the assumption that you over-breathe at least some of the time. To get relief from anxiety, sleep better and function better, you need to breathe less – at least when under stress but probably generally. The cloud concept will help you do that.

Visualise your total daily air consumption as a cloud. See Figure 5.1. Over the next 24 hours, and starting right now, think about reducing the total volume of air you breathe by just 1–5 per cent compared to what you breathed yesterday. That means it is to be a very gentle and comfortable change.

Looking at the cloud image, the outer line is your cloud size in the previous 24 hours. The second line, just a little inside the first, represents the slightly smaller volume of air you will consume in the next 24 hours. The following 24 hours, you shrink it again.

How will you do this?

FIGURE 5.1: THE CLOUD EXERCISE

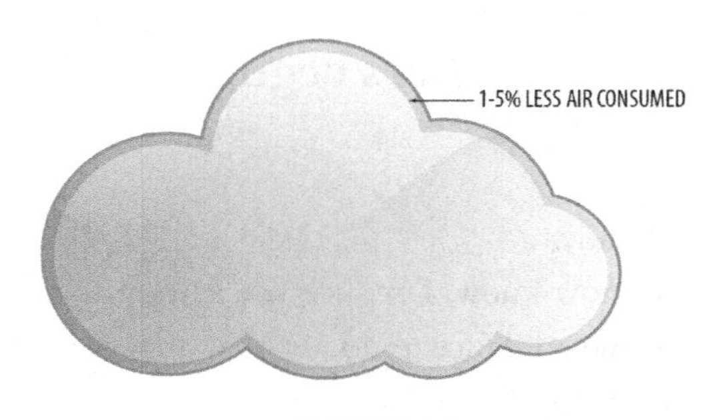

"SHRINKING YOUR CLOUD"

The Cloud Exercise – 'shrinking your cloud'

1) Breathe more gently than you have been, with the idea of consuming 1–5 per cent less air today than you did yesterday.
   a) **Nose breathers**
   Try to breathe more gently through your nose. Stay comfortable. Allow yourself satisfying nose breaths, but not the extra air that you don't need.
   b) **Mouth breathers (sometimes)**
   Aim to breathe through your nose more today than you did yesterday – whenever nose breathing feels comfortable. Because the size of your two nostrils together is much less than that of your mouth, whenever you are nose breathing you will take in less air than when mouth breathing.
   c) **Mouth breathers (nose is congested)**
   If your nose is congested or you find it uncomfortable to breathe through it, then you can still try a 1–5 per cent reduction in the amount of air you breathe, each day, by *breathing more gently through your mouth.* That is, take smaller mouth breaths. You are

still reducing over-breathing, and this automatically helps clear your nose, so keep trying your nose out!

2) If you sigh or yawn a lot, try to reduce the volume of your sighs/yawns by stifling them or cutting them short.

If you are a chronic mouth breather, you may need to make the transition to nose breathing very slowly the first few days. Remember, this practice should cause no discomfort. Make the changes gentle.

Continue to progressively increase the total time you nose breathe each day and keep this cloud shrinking as you read on. You should soon feel the benefits. If you are not fully nose breathing by the time you get to the full program in Part Two, further strategies to help you are given in Chapter 13.

Elyse was, in her own words, "stressed to the eyeballs". Panic attacks ruled her life. She was having four or five a week. She knew she was 'on the edge' the day she came to see me. All I introduced was the cloud concept. That night she slept without a nightmare, the first time in as long as she could remember. Well rested and calm, she was ready for more when I saw her two days later. Overall, she had a 47 per cent reduction in 'Symptom Score' simply from practising 'shrinking her cloud'.

The key words here are: *Gentle* | *Comfortable* | *Nose* | *1–5 per cent less air*.
The golden rules are: *Breathe a little less* | *Breathe more gently* | *No discomfort*

ACTION STEPS FOR FIRST STEPS AND CLOUD EXERCISE

- Visualise your cloud – your 24-hour air consumption.
- Shrink your cloud 1–5 per cent per day for a few days.
- Breathe more gently – mouth or nose.
- Breathe through your nose - whenever comfortable to do so.

Why so little? Can't I do more?

Sometimes, you have to go slowly before you go fast and far. Trust me, I'm an observer and teacher of thousands of people who live life on roller blades. You need to retrain…S L O W L Y…at least at first.

CHAPTER 6

The over-breathing model – explaining anxiety disorders

Anxiety is a combination of emotions and physiological disturbances (physical and chemical). While emotions may kick-start anxiety, anxiety will always have a physiological basis as well. It is here where most misunderstanding lies.

The medical focus has been on brain neurotransmitter and hormone levels, with inconclusive arguments about how they are involved (cause or effect?) and the exact balance you need. Faulty baseline breathing as a primary cause has been overlooked.

With the talking therapies, over-breathing/hyperventilation is a well-recognised factor in acute anxiety episodes, but again, faulty everyday breathing is overlooked.

An explanation that makes sense

When first hearing the idea that incorrect breathing can cause anxiety, some people question the relevance for them. The blame may have been placed fully on major life stress, a traumatic experience, low self-esteem, or a genetic tendency. Or they may believe they are a hopeless case because their doctor has said they have a 'chemical imbalance' in their brain and they will need medication for the rest of their life.

In this chapter, I present the over-breathing model for anxiety disorders. This model does not contradict current mainstream theories but rather adds to them and explains inconsistencies and anomalies that confuse them.

OVER-BREATHING IS COMMON IN PEOPLE WITH ANXIETY DISORDERS

If we gathered a roomful of people who have anxiety disorders, some would be over 70, some under 10; some would have stressful jobs, some would be retired; some would be rich and some poor. Only some would have a family history of anxiety; some would have had childhood trauma; many, but not all, would have had a major stressful event. None are likely to have had a biochemical imbalance in their brain scientifically verified. The one factor they would all have in common, although it would vary in severity, is a physiologically abnormal breathing pattern. Research shows that an over-breathing pattern is characteristic in people with anxiety disorders. An average minute volume of 12 litres per minute has been found [6.1] and an average respiratory rate of over 18 breaths per minute.[6.2]

PHYSIOLOGY EXPLAINS THE OVER-BREATHING–ANXIETY/PANIC LINK

One of the most important changes caused by over-breathing is constriction of blood vessels in parts of the body, notably those to the brain. The dizziness, light-headedness and confusion classically seen during panic attacks are consistent with low brain oxygen (hypoxia) caused by over-breathing.[6.3, 6.4] Ball and Shekhar (1992) found an average reduction in blood flow to the brain of 55 per cent when panic patients hyperventilated.[6.5] Physiology also explains the link between over-breathing and the many other psychological and physical symptoms commonly seen with anxiety disorders. The explanations given here are kept as simple as possible. Those wanting to explore the science further are directed to the texts and journal articles listed in Chapter References and Resource Material on page 195.

Anxiety and panic attack snapshot

You breathe faster. Your heart races and pounds, your palms become sweaty, your muscles tense or shake, your mind becomes singularly focused on the anxiety-causing event and confused about anything else. Adrenalin pours into your system and you enter the fight-or-flight state.

It's appropriate to breathe more when you are 'fighting' or 'fleeing' because your need for oxygen increases. At the same time, carbon dioxide production increases in your fighting or running muscles and you have more carbon dioxide to exhale. However, this is not a normal response to a deadline at work or to driving across a high bridge. In these situations, oxygen needs and carbon dioxide levels in your blood are *not* increased. High-volume breathing here creates a sharp fall in blood-carbon dioxide levels, which can set off a chemical cascade in your body and a panic attack.[1] The anxiety response diminishes our ability to think creatively and increases our distress rather than improving it.

If we look at the roles of carbon dioxide, we understand why bad things can happen when we blow out too much of it. Not just the brain stuff, but the distressing or weird symptoms all over the body, like dripping armpits, tingling legs, diarrhoea, and feeling as if you have a vice around your chest. After all, carbon dioxide is a chemical, and through over-breathing you can significantly alter the level of it in your body.

Carbon dioxide – not just a waste gas

Far from being a waste gas, carbon dioxide has many important roles as a governor of body functions and processes, including blood flow to the brain.

Carbon dioxide:

- relaxes smooth muscle in the walls of your airways, bladder, uterus, gastrointestinal tract, and blood vessels [6.4]
- is the body's natural bronchodilator and antihistamine[6.6]
- assists blood flow and oxygen transport by relaxing blood vessels[6.4]
- gets oxygen into the cells by 'unsticking' the oxygen from the red blood cells (Bohr effect)
- enhances digestion by relaxing the walls of the gut
- balances and regulates pH; it is the body's number one 'buffer'.
- has a sedative effect on the nervous system
- plays an important role in electrolyte balance and metabolism
- plays an important role in synthesis and regulation of antibodies, hormones and enzymes
- regulates your breathing through receptors in the 'respiratory centre' of the brainstem.

---

1 The theory behind the practice of breathing through cupped hands or into a paper bag to calm a panic attack is that you are able to reabsorb some of the lost carbon dioxide.

Carbon dioxide is a relaxant

An easy way of remembering the above is simply to think of carbon dioxide as a relaxant. It relaxes your blood vessels, your airways, the wall of your gut and bladder, your nerves, and your muscles. And it's free, you make it yourself. You've just got to stop blowing it all out into the atmosphere.

The more you breathe the less oxygen you get

With over-breathing, you end up with less oxygen in your brain, heart and elsewhere instead of more, for two reasons: because blood vessels constrict, and because when carbon dioxide drops too low, the bond between the oxygen and its carriers – the red blood cells – tightens. Oxygen clings to the red blood cells, less is released, and tissues, especially the brain, become starved of oxygen. This is called the 'Bohr effect'. Paradoxically, then, with over-breathing, oxygen is plentiful in the blood but less of it is delivered to the brain and other areas of your body. You become hypoxic – low in oxygen.

LOW CARBON DIOXIDE EFFECTS

The effects of low carbon dioxide include:

- nerve cells become agitated → spasm, twitching, hyperarousal
- histamine is released into the bloodstream → allergic response, inflammation
- smooth muscle tightens around airways → bronchospasm, breathing difficulties
- oxygen becomes more tightly bound to red blood cells and less gets to tissues
- smooth muscle tightens around certain blood vessels, reducing blood flow → dizziness, fainting, panic (reduced oxygen to the brain) → myocardial ischaemia (reduced oxygen to the heart muscle)
- smooth muscle tightens around the gut → poor digestion, colic, irritable bowel
- acute alkalosis (sudden rise in pH) → pins and needles, numbness, palpitations
- extra sugar released into the bloodstream → blood sugar irregularities
- adrenaline pumped throughout the body
- anaerobic metabolism increases → lactic acid, muscle soreness, fatigue
- increased seizure activity
- arrhythmia (disturbance in heart rhythm)
- general muscle tension, cramps and muscle twitches.

Blow off your carbon dioxide at your peril!

The brain and heart are such heavy users of oxygen that the harmful effects of over-breathing are often noticed there first. Less oxygen reaching the heart can result in increased heart rate, chest pain or discomfort, palpitations, and high blood pressure. Feeling dizzy and light-headed is a sign of low oxygen in the brain. Have you ever felt like this when you were blowing up balloons quickly, or after taking big breaths in a yoga or Pilates class? Over-breathing can reduce oxygen supply to the brain by 40 per cent or more, causing an outpouring of adrenaline and more anxiety, and making it difficult to concentrate.

Elsewhere in the body, you may feel changes in oxygen delivery as coldness, numbness and tingling.

Are you starving yourself of oxygen by breathing too much?

FIGURE 6.1: EFFECTS OF OVER-BREATHING ON THE BRAIN

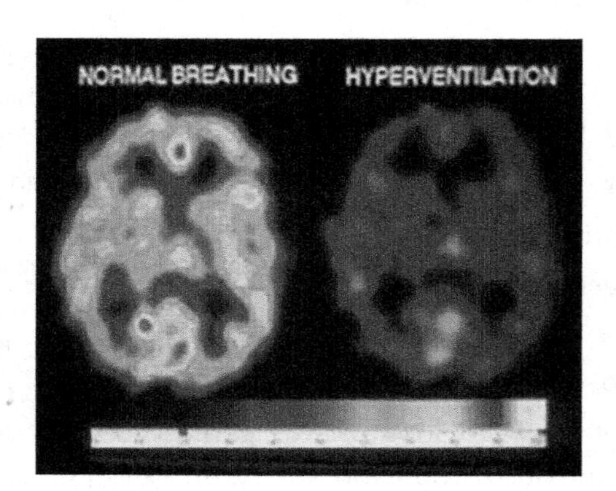

BRAIN SCAN SHOWING 40% LESS OXYGEN AFTER ONE MINUTE OF OVER-BREATHING

Image courtesty of Dr P M. Litchfield, Grad School of Behavioral Health Sciences, Wyoming USA. (1999)

Anxious 22-year-old Cheri had been having four or five fainting episodes a week for three months. Before she fainted she had double vision, tingling in her hands and feet, extreme dizziness, and she found it hard to breathe. Tests with a cardiologist and a neurologist found nothing abnormal – which was both good and bad. Good in that she didn't have heart disease, epilepsy or multiple sclerosis and she hadn't had a stroke, but not so good because her scary symptoms were 'unexplainable'. The second neurologist she saw did explain them. He noticed that she took lots of deep breaths and sighed a lot. A referral for breathing retraining solved the problems.

Carbon dioxide relaxes the nervous system

Carbon dioxide has a calming and stabilising effect on nerve cells and your *autonomic nervous system*. This system regulates many unconscious functions that keep you alive, for example, digestion, breathing, heart rate, perspiration, blood pressure. It is divided into two: a *sympathetic, fight-or-flight* or 'get-up-and-go' branch, and a *parasympathetic* rest, digest and 'chill-out' branch.

When carbon dioxide is low, the sympathetic nervous system is stimulated more than the parasympathetic: nerve cells become excitable and agitated. A state of nervousness and muscle tension results.

SYMPATHETIC NERVOUS SYSTEM – FIGHT-OR-FLIGHT

The sympathetic nervous system activates the fight-or-flight response. This is where your body reacts to an emergency situation or a threat. For example, you are out for a walk and a vicious dog starts growling at you. Your body reacts with an adrenaline, cortisol and blood-sugar surge, gearing you up to counter the danger with immediate physical activity – wrestling the dog or running away fast. This is a great reaction to have when your survival is threatened. The fight-or-flight response is a human survival system, a natural physiological response to threat. It is a wonderfully adaptive response, but when switched on all the time it ceases to be protective because everything is perceived as a threat.

In hunter-gatherer times, a threat usually involved a physical response. The extra sugar in the bloodstream got used up as fuel, and plenty of carbon dioxide was produced in the working muscles of the fighter or fleer to balance the amount being lost with quicker, deeper breathing. Blood chemistry stayed in balance. And the emergency situation resolved quickly. Either you killed the wild animal or it killed you.

In today's world, your only physical activity when the fight-or-flight response is invoked may be your fingers moving across the keyboard as you type an email to your boss to say you've missed a deadline. Pumping heart, fast breathing and dripping armpits here are like being 'all dressed up with nowhere to go'. Such stimulation is damaging if it becomes a habitual state for your body. It's like having an overzealous bodyguard on your case 24/7, or a fire alarm going off constantly. You end up feeling wired, spaced out, anxious, or panicky.

Second stage symptoms

If you maintain hyperventilation, you may go into a second stage where you have nausea or diarrhoea, feel a smothering inability to breathe, sharp pains in your chest, temporary paralysis of muscles in different parts of your body, dread that something terrible is going to happen, and momentary loss of consciousness (blackout). These well-recognised symptoms of panic attacks are also classic symptoms of *hyperventilation syndrome.* (Refer Table 3.1, page 24.)

Sympathetic fight-or-flight response:

- Heart rate increases.
- Breathing rate and volume increases.
- Sweating begins or increases.
- The adrenal glands pump out adrenaline and cortisol.
- Blood sugar levels increase quickly.
- Blood supply to internal organs diverts to arms and legs.

PARASYMPATHETIC NERVOUS SYSTEM – REST AND DIGEST

The parasympathetic nervous system governs the relaxation response. It is concerned with repair and maintenance of the body and plays a role in the immune system. It also oversees digestion – the flow of saliva, digestive juices and enzymes. When it's dominant, you feel relaxed, on the inside and the outside. Digestion can start, your blood pressure decreases.

Parasympathetic rest and digest response:

- Heart rate decreases.
- Blood pressure reduces.
- Breathing slows.
- Digestion is stimulated.
- Muscles relax.

Chronic over-breathing = sympathetic dominant

In those with a normal anxiety response, once an anxiety-causing event has passed, the sympathetic and parasympathetic nervous systems return the body to normal functioning. However, 21st-century stressors are often psychological and may persist for days, months or even years. Without knowing it, you can maintain a degree of over-breathing all the time, and be 'sympathetic dominant', experiencing significant anxiety and stress even when no immediate danger is present. The sympathetic nervous system is in overdrive; you have your foot resting on the accelerator, stress hormones coursing through you. Exhaustion, poor sleep, feelings of mental and physical depression soon follow – classic symptoms of chronic over-breathing.

Do you have any signs of being sympathetic dominant? Jot them down here.

____

____

____

____

The more air you usually breathe, and the lower your usual carbon dioxide level is, the closer you may be to the tipping point. That is when a relatively minor stimulus – such as feelings, sugar, caffeine, street drugs, noise, difficult neighbours, work problems, health worries, or perhaps nothing at all – tips you into your particular symptom pattern. Everyone has different limits. What makes you nervous and sweaty may be boring to someone else.

Your adrenal glands, the small 2cm x 3cm glands that sit above your kidneys, can become tired or exhausted if you stay sympathetic dominant. Signs of adrenal exhaustion are weight gain, anxiety and depression, immune suppression, insomnia, and fatigue.

Normal breathing facilitates parasympathetic relaxation response

You will have much more stable blood and brain chemistry if you learn to control your breathing in acute situations and optimise your baseline breathing, that is, your everyday breathing, in the long term. You will take your foot off the accelerator and the adrenaline pump. Nose breathing and gentle breathing both promote the parasympathetic nervous system.

OVER-BREATHING, NEUROTRANSMITTERS AND HORMONES

The neurotransmitters dopamine and serotonin are associated with mood control and clarity of thinking. Serotonin also plays a part in sleep regulation. Persistent stress and persistent over-breathing will increase the production of the stress hormones adrenaline and cortisol. They in turn influence the neurotransmitters, and other hormones such as oestrogen and oxytocin. The result can be imbalances in neurotransmitter and hormone levels.

Neglecting to do something about faulty breathing and relying on drug therapy alone to sort out these brain chemicals does not make sense. Also, a person may not have the strength to begin or benefit from counselling or a talking therapy until they first support their nervous system by sorting their breathing out.

Ben was a charming, easy-going, intelligent young man – and anxious all the time. He had lost his mother when he was nine years old. He fronted up to work each day and no-one guessed how difficult he found it to leave his desk and tasks and join in and contribute to team projects. His continual colds were the only visible sign of his body's stress. There was no way he would see a counsellor. Just the thought of it knotted him up inside.

Once Ben began to support his adrenals and nervous system through better breathing, his respiratory symptoms cleared and he felt a growing confidence 'on the inside' in meetings and social situations. He was reassured to find that the sharp pains in his chest, which woke him several times a month, never reoccurred.

OVER-BREATHING AND GENETIC TENDENCIES

While the potential for mental illness may be in your genes, whether the illness manifests or not depends on other factors. For example, if your breathing rate increases as part of the stress response to a major life stress, financial problems or physical illness, the chemical cascade of the fight-or-flight response could be the tipping factor to a genetic predisposition manifesting. The work of Herbert Benson and colleagues has proven conclusively that the opposite response, the relaxation response, can switch off genetic expression.[6,7]

OVER-BREATHING: OVER-LOOKED

You may be wondering why until now, you've never heard that the way you breathe plays a part in anxiety. I believe there are several reasons for this. First, screening for a dysfunctional breathing pattern is not part of standard medical diagnosis. Second, the primary focus in current medical treatment appears to be medication for a 'brain chemistry imbalance' more than on actually preventing the disturbance. Last, it seems that today we can be so disconnected from our bodies and so used to popping a pill for everything, or handing over our problems to the 'experts', that we do not look closely at ourselves for the source of a problem or its solution.

What do you think might happen if you retrained the breathing-control centre in your brain and turned the dial down a bit?

FIGURE 6.3: RESETTING YOUR 'DRIVE TO BREATHE'

Ultimately, the volume of air you breathe and the stability or otherwise of your breathing when you are under stress are central to whether you will develop anxiety symptoms or panic attacks, and how intense they will be.

Note: implicating over-breathing as a primary factor in many instances of anxiety and panic does not discount psychological, biochemical or metabolic causes, or cases where psychological therapy and medications are essential to responsible management. The best management, however, may well be a combination of these approaches.

SUMMARY OF OVER-BREATHING MODEL FOR ANXIETY DISORDERS

Dysfunctional breathing and over-breathing are characteristic of the breathing pattern of people with anxiety and panic disorders.

A loss of carbon dioxide from the body through over-breathing:

- alters blood and brain chemistry (pH)
- affects neurotransmitter and hormone levels
- compromises delivery and uptake of oxygen by cells and tissues throughout the body
- promotes high sympathetic drive (fight-or-flight response)
- affects every system of the body, producing psychological and physical symptoms commonly associated with anxiety disorders.

When you improve your breathing, it is not just your anxiety symptoms that are likely to improve.

In the next chapter, we look more closely at the connection between over-breathing and other symptoms and conditions commonly seen in people with anxiety disorders.

ACTION STEPS

- Continue to 'shrink your cloud' each day.
- Breathe gently, breathe less generally.
- Favour nose breathing or more gentle mouth breathing.

CHAPTER 7

Not just the head stuff – explaining those other symptoms

Here I explain the link between over-breathing and some common symptoms and conditions associated with anxiety disorders. Genetic predispositions are important in determining which systems or organs of your body may be affected. It's obvious why improving the way you breathe can have such all-round benefits.

Look at the headings below. Skip any sections that don't apply to you.

BREATHING DIFFICULTIES, SHORTNESS OF BREATH

Breathing difficulties include shortness of breath, feeling that your breathing is restricted, that you are suffocating, or even that your chest is being crushed. These are all common in people with anxiety. There are several effects of over-breathing/low carbon dioxide that are relevant here. Over-breathing can cause tightness in the smooth muscles around the breathing tubes (bronchioles) and provoke the release of histamine and mucus in your airways. This inflames and narrows the passages, interfering with the delivery of oxygen.

Also, when you use your upper-chest muscles to breathe, you probably feel even more deprived of air, as these muscles fatigue easily. Your chest wall can become sore to touch because of muscle fatigue and lactic acid build-up.

Some people who over-breathe say they can never get enough air, no matter how deeply they breathe. Paradoxically, their breathing becomes more comfortable when they learn to breathe less.

Nine-year-old Jack was referred to me because he was breathless all the time and doctors could find no trace of asthma. A major clue was that he had been snoring for many years and was a 100 per cent mouth breather. With breathing retraining, Jack became a 100 per cent nose breather within days, playing basketball without losing his breath and running faster than ever before.

Are you gently shrinking your breathing as you are reading? 

NASAL AND THROAT PROBLEMS

Over-breathing is like physical abuse of your airways. The tissues lining your nose, sinuses, throat, and lungs can become dehydrated, inflamed and swollen and produce mucus.[7.1, 7.2] The result can be a blocked, stuffy or runny nose, post-nasal drip, the growth of nasal or sinus polyps, enlarged adenoids, and painful, congested sinus passages. You may often feel you have to mouth breathe to be comfortable.

WHAT'S WRONG WITH MOUTH BREATHING?

Mouth breathing may contribute to:

- bad breath, dental decay, gum disease
- narrowing of the dental arch, jaw and palate
- crowded and crooked teeth and open bite
- greater potential for relapse of orthodontic corrections
- poor facial aesthetics, elongated face
- loss of lip tone, with the lips becoming larger and more flaccid
- noisy eating, speech and swallow-ing problems
- introducing unfiltered, poorly humidified air into your lungs
- inflamed and enlarged tonsils and adenoids
- over-breathing → increased incidence asthma, anxiety, snoring, sleep apnoea.

MOUTH BREATHING

Mouth breathing is over-breathing. Not only do you miss out on the air-conditioning and filtering properties of the nose, but the tidal volume of air you breathe can increase significantly without your realising. This results in more severe over-breathing symptoms.

In children, persistent mouth breathing results in unnatural constrictive forces on the bone structures of the face. It is associated with the development of a narrow elongated face, narrow nose and upper jaw, crooked and crowded teeth, and snoring and sleep apnoea.

When you recondition your breathing and become more comfortable with nose breathing, slower breathing and taking in less air, then you reduce the irritation and trauma to your nasal tissues, adenoids and tonsils. These tissues have the potential to heal. Even polyps can shrink. With less inflammation, there is more space to breathe through.

Restoring nose breathing is usually the first thing breathing retraining addresses.

How are you going with it?

'ATYPICAL' CHEST PAINS, PALPITATIONS

Cardiologists frequently see patients with anxiety who complain of chest pain and palpitations. When clinical testing fails to find any evidence of coronary artery disease, hyperventilation should be suspected.[7.1]

Understanding the effects of over-breathing/low carbon dioxide on blood flow, oxygen release and the autonomic nervous system makes it clear why there can be repercussions on the heart. (The autonomic nervous system is responsible for 'automatic' bodily functions like breathing, the heartbeat and digestion.)

Terry was a public servant in his 50s who had suffered with anxiety for several years. When he became troubled by recurring chest pain, an exercise stress test by his cardiologist did not show any problem with blood flow to his heart. Terry was then referred to me. When he arrived at reception for his first appointment, I could hear his rapid heavy breathing from my consultation room. Terry's chest pains resolved after his first breathing retraining session. So did his chronic anxiety.

SLEEP DISORDERS

Sleep is vitally important for your mental, emotional and physical wellbeing. Even one night of disrupted sleep can lead to irritability, poor concentration, and slow reflexes and decision-making. It undermines your ability to regulate your emotions the next day.

Sleep disorders and depression

Sleep disorders significantly increase your risk of depression. A study of nearly 10,000 Australians found that young women with regular sleep problems have a four to five-fold increased risk of depression.[7.3]

The most common sleep disorders are snoring and sleep apnoea. Sleep apnoea is a serious condition where breathing stops temporarily and repeatedly during sleep.

Snoring: The connection with over-breathing is rather obvious here. Snoring is the noise you make as you breathe a lot of air quickly through your airway during sleep, when your throat muscles are relaxed. This high-velocity breathing causes turbulence and vibration of the soft tissues in your throat, creating the snoring noise. There is definitely not a normal tidal volume going in and out during snoring! Anyone who has slept downstream of a heavy snorer will identify with this. One woman described her partner's snoring this way: "when he breathes in it's like he's sucking the paint off the walls; when he breathes out I have to hold on to the edge of the bed so he doesn't blow me out." Over-breathing can also dehydrate and inflame the soft tissues in your nose and throat, making the problem even worse.

Sleep apnoea: By breathing in fast or heavily enough you may drop your carbon dioxide level so much that the signal to breathe will fail. Breathing stops for a while until the carbon dioxide has been sufficiently replenished to kick-start breathing again. This is called *central sleep apnoea. Obstructive sleep apnoea* is where the flow of air to the lungs temporarily stops because the airway is obstructed. This can be because of enlarged tonsils and adenoids, your jaw dropping back when mouth breathing, and by breathing in fast and heavily enough that you suck the walls of your throat close together. It's not unlike sucking too hard on a straw. After a period of time, which can be as long as a minute or more, breathing starts again, often with a snort or choking sound.

Sleep can be disrupted hundreds of times in just one night, and sufferers may be prevented from spending adequate time in the deep, restorative sleep stage. Blood pressure can increase and there are changes in heart rate and rhythm associated with apnoea episodes. Sufferers may experience debilitating fatigue and other serious health conditions. Even snoring without apnoea is linked to a greater risk of high blood pressure and stroke.

Research has shown sleep apnoea sufferers averaging 15 litres of air a minute,[7.4] three times as much as a healthy breather. And this is during the day, which sets them up for what happens at night.

There is substantial clinical evidence that reducing over-breathing through breathing retraining can prevent snoring and sleep apnoea.[7.5; 7.6]

Note: Sleep apnoea is a serious medical condition. If you have not already been medically diagnosed with sleep apnoea and suspect that you have it, see your doctor.

Insomnia

Insomnia means difficulty falling asleep, staying asleep or returning to sleep if awakened. It is estimated that up to 25 per cent of the population suffer from insomnia at some stage of their lives, and about 10 per cent have chronic insomnia.

Is there a connection with over-breathing? There certainly is. Over-breathing excites your brain and makes muscles tense. It can therefore aggravate and even trigger insomnia.

Insomnia can respond well to the calming effects of controlled breathing. Remember, carbon dioxide is a natural sedative and muscle relaxant. Having adequate levels is important in falling asleep and staying asleep. There is a special section on insomnia and how to reduce it in Chapter 23.

DIZZINESS, VISUAL DISTURBANCES, NUMBNESS, TINGLING

Neurologists frequently see patients describing dizziness, unsteadiness, fainting, blurred vision, vertigo, and paraesthesia. The latter refers to abnormal skin sensations in the limbs, like tingling, pricking and creeping. These symptoms relate to disturbances in blood flow and oxygenation and are classic symptoms of over-breathing and *hyperventilation syndrome*.

Cassie, a 23-year-old student had been an anxious teenager. For six months now she had episodes of double vision, muscle weakness in her legs and tingling and numbness in her face, arms and legs. The symptoms occurred on average four times a week and lasted around five hours. Her neurologist could find nothing wrong on EEG and nerve conduction tests so suspected hyperventilation and sent her to see me. The first thing I noticed was her slumped posture, then her erratic upper-chest breathing, punctuated with sighs and prolonged pauses. Cassie commenced breathing retraining that day. She had no further tingling and numbness. Her sleep improved and she felt strong again, and altogether calmer.

Are you remembering to breathe more gently while you are reading?

HEADACHES

Headaches have various causes, but one is certainly related to breathing. Headaches can happen when there are changes in the tone – constriction (tightening) and dilation (stretching) – of arteries feeding the brain. Because carbon dioxide affects the tone of the wall of arteries, fluctuations in carbon dioxide with erratic breathing may cause you to suffer with headaches. Significant reduction in headaches is reported following breathing retraining.

FREQUENT TOILET VISITS

Needing to urinate frequently is common in anxiety sufferers. How does that work? When you over-breathe, the drop in blood carbon dioxide increases tension in smooth muscle, including that in the wall of the bladder. The increase in pressure on the bladder drives the need to urinate. In addition, there are changes in pH and electrolyte levels that may increase urine production.

If you hyperventilate during sleep, you disrupt the natural sleep cycles, including the production of ADH (anti-diuretic hormone), which enables your body to concentrate urine.

One of the first things many people notice when they improve their breathing is a reduction in daytime and night-time toilet trips.

John came to the breathing class in the hope of putting an end to his snoring, which was driving his wife crazy. The snoring wasn't bothering him, but having to get up to go to the toilet three times a night certainly was. He thought there was something wrong with his bladder or, even worse, his prostate. John hadn't yet got around to doing anything about it, but three nights into the breathing course he started to sleep right through the night. John was happy, and so was his wife!

DIGESTIVE UPSET, IRRITABLE BOWEL, 'NERVOUS STOMACH'

The nerves regulating digestion appear to be hypersensitive to stimulation. As stated earlier, nerve hypersensitivity (sympathetic dominance) is a classic effect of over-breathing. So too is smooth muscle spasm. This is the type of muscle in the wall of your digestive tract.

Over-breathing can cause the nerves and muscle fibres of your stomach and small intestine to malfunction. This interferes with the secretion of several chemical substances needed for proper digestion (including serotonin) and the movement of the intestinal tract. The result can be nausea, indigestion, heartburn, colic, bloating, and flatulence. Your intestinal tract will move slower (constipation) or faster (diarrhoea) than it should. It is almost impossible to feel well if your gut is upset, which only adds to your anxiety.

If your doctor has ruled out a harmful disease that is the cause of your bowel symptoms, then attention to your breathing is likely to deliver a great outcome here.

BLOOD SUGAR ISSUES

Remember that over-breathing and hypoxia cause an outpouring of adrenaline. As a result, loads of glucose (sugar) can be dumped into your bloodstream. When sugar is not used up by immediate physical activity, the excess can be stored as fat. To add to your troubles, you are at increased risk of weight gain and blood sugar disorders.

SEXUAL PROBLEMS

As if anxiety sufferers didn't already have enough to worry about, there is now growing evidence to suggest they also have higher rates of sexual problems. And it's not just stress, worries, fatigue, and low mood that affect sexual relationships. Sexual arousal is controlled by the parasympathetic or relaxation part of your autonomic nervous system. If you are over-breathing, the sympathetic part is dominant, which will prevent proper neural response during the arousal stage of sexual intimacy.

Some anxiety sufferers develop a fear of having sex. The sexual act involves an increase in adrenaline, breathing rate and heart rate and this can trigger feelings of panic for some. Short-term hyperventilation during the sexual act is natural, but when you already have a degree of baseline over-breathing, the resulting feelings can be most unpleasant. Getting your baseline breathing right can reduce anxiety levels and bring back sexual enjoyment.

References 7.7–7.9 (page 196), provide background reading on hyperventilation and its effects throughout the body. Now you have even more reason to reduce over-breathing!

By now, you may be wondering how your breathing got off track in the first place. I will take you through a few of the reasons in the next chapter.

ACTION STEPS

- Continue to shrink your cloud.
- Try to breathe through your nose when you walk.
- Slow down your walking to the pace at which you can breathe comfortably in and out your nose.

Your nose breathing must not be noisy, uncomfortable or distressed. You will be a bit slower at first, but it usually doesn't take long to get back to your old pace, except with much better breathing control.

CHAPTER 8

Why me? How disordered breathing starts

You are not alone! There are many imperfect breathers out there. Over 50 per cent of adults and children mouth breathe at least some of the time, and the average breathing rate among adults is around double the ideal.

While breathing is largely automatic, it is also affected by stress and emotions; by physical and environmental factors including posture, diet, medications, air quality, and breathing techniques you may have practised – for example, in sport training, yoga, Pilates, or singing lessons. So there can be any number of reasons your baseline, habitual, automatic breathing pattern is what it is today.

Poor breathing habits often develop over time without us realising. Like any habit, they are formed through repetition. They can start very early – three-year-olds can snore, eight-year-olds can be constantly yawning and twelve-year-olds can be chest-breathing. From my observations, around 50 per cent of primary school children mouth breathe every day. When a stress or inadvertent practice of incorrect breathing persists over time, the abnormal pattern becomes embedded as a new habit: a faulty breathing habit. You are often unaware of it.

Resetting your breathing auto-pilot

Your breathing is automatically regulated by the 'respiratory centre' – a special group of cells (carbon dioxide receptors) in your brainstem. It is like an auto-pilot. If through over-breathing you maintain lower than normal carbon dioxide over a critical period of time, the receptors adjust their carbon dioxide 'set point'.[8.1 - 8.3] You have a new breathing set point now and it is abnormal. The lower your carbon dioxide set point, the closer you are

to the 'edge' - the point at which you lose your balance and fall into physical and psychological symptoms.

WHAT'S BEHIND TODAY'S HIGH INCIDENCE OF DYSFUNCTIONAL BREATHING?

Why are so many, so often in a state of sympathetic overdrive? The three main reasons as I see it are:

- 21st-century stress and lifestyle
- ignorance and misinformation about breathing
- inflammatory diet

21st century stress and lifestyle

High stress levels and modern lifestyles get our brains firing and elevate our breathing and heart rate. Many people today live in a state of sympathetic overdrive, fuelling a pattern of over-breathing.

When high stress levels accompany a sedentary lifestyle, this over-stimulation is not counterbalanced by physical activity. Workaholics, high achievers, people with big mortgages, financial problems or relationship breakdown, carers, students, refugees, the bereaved, or workers made redundant, to name just a few, can potentially develop a stress-related breathing pattern disorder.

Add to this the modern-day obsession with all things electronic – smart devices, gaming, laptops – and it can lead to information overload and overwhelm. Not only are we always 'switched on', we are exposed to a lot of electromagnetic radiation which has been linked to anxiety, insomnia, poor sleep, and hormonal imbalance. Add to that the slumped sitting posture of the office worker, the texting teenager and the television watcher and we have another major culprit in the development of an upper-chest over-breathing habit.

Ignorance and misinformation about breathing

Myths and misunderstanding about breathing abound. The worst of them is the widely-held belief that the deeper and fuller we breathe, the better. Secondly, that carbon dioxide is a toxic waste gas and we should empty as much as possible from our lungs.

This misinformation has led many people to a long-term habit or frequent practice of overly filling and emptying their lungs of air. In addition, an over-effort to maintain a flat stomach or improve core stability by consciously tensing the abdominal muscles interferes with the movement of the diaphragm, and therefore your breathing, and may potentially induce an upper-chest breathing pattern.

CIRCUMSTANCES THAT MAY LEAD TO HABITUALLY DISORDERED BREATHING

If prolonged, the following can lead to habitually disordered breathing:

- over-stimulation
- high stress levels
- emotional stress/shock
- chemicals in the environment
- chronic pain, chronic illness
- mouth breathing habit
- bad posture
- 'too-deep' breathing exercises
- forced exhalation exercises
- excessive crying (children)
- exercise with poor breath control
- recurrent colds and infections, chronic cough
- high sugar/high starch diet
- overeating
- poor nutrition
- high caffeine intake
- excessive alcohol consumption

Inflammatory diet

From my observation, poor dietary choices, in particular high-inflammatory foods, are a significant cause of dysfunctional breathing. The sympathetic nervous system is activated by consuming these foods when it should only be activated during a fight-or-flight situation, not while you are having your lunch.

The modern diet with its heavy bias towards sugar, additive-laden and processed foods, and highly refined carbohydrates, has a lot to answer for. This food connection to breathing and anxiety, and what you can do to help yourself, are so important that the next chapter is devoted to it.

Note: An increased respiratory drive can also be caused by or be part of the body's way of compensating for certain conditions such as anaemia, diabetes, renal acidosis, liver failure, chronic obstructive pulmonary disorder (COPD), or morbid obesity. If you have any doubt about your particular situation, check with your doctor. (Also see Important note in the Introduction, page IX.)

Some things to think about

- How many items in the list on page 61 are relevant to you?
- How much emotional, environmental or physical stress have you been exposed to? Has it been consistent enough to affect your breathing pattern?
- How much practice of deep, full breathing have you done?

NG

You may be living 'on the edge'. It does not take much to tip you over into fear, confusion, apprehension, or a full-on panic attack. It may only take added work stress or family responsibility, a minor upset, a broken washing machine, the internet going down. It's as if your nervous system is trigger-happy; your fuse is shortened.

Lauren, a mum of three children under five, had just moved her family interstate. Her husband couldn't join them for several days. After two days on the road, the first thing she did when she arrived at their rented house was put the dirty clothes into the washing machine and... they got trapped inside. It was her first experience of a front-loader and the machine stopped mid-cycle. Lauren was unable to open the door and retrieve the only clothes she had on hand, as the removalist truck had not arrived yet.

Minor problem? Yes, in the scheme of things, but this was the family's third employment-related move in seven months, with a new-born and no extended family or friend support. An anxiety state in the form of a complete inability to think, plan and act overwhelmed her. On automatic pilot, she phoned her doctor from a previous life (two moves previously) who sent a calm local mother of four to help her.

You don't have to work out 'what started it?' to succeed at breathing retraining. Adjusting your breathing acts like a circuit breaker. By reducing your day-to-day over-breathing, you can bring your carbon dioxide setpoint closer to normal. It is similar to broadening the path you walk on through life. Rather than walking fearfully on a narrow path, near an edge, where the slightest upset can make you lose your balance, by having your breathing and carbon dioxide balanced, you too are balanced and resilient. The things that used to be your triggers don't bother you anymore.

One of the best moves you can make to help your breathing is to look at the foods you eat. Which ones are feeding your over-breathing habit? The information in the next chapter has had a profound positive impact on thousands of people with anxiety issues.

ACTION STEPS

- Continue to shrink your cloud each day.
- Breathe gently.
- Favour nose breathing or more gentle mouth breathing.
- Walk with nose breathing or more gentle mouth breathing.
- Slow down if necessary.

CHAPTER 9

The food connection

Poor dietary choices are, from my observations, a major cause of over-breathing and gut dysfunction, which are both strongly linked to mental health disorders. Significantly, many of the comfort foods anxious people choose may considerably worsen their breathing and mental health issues.

Increasingly, since the 1950s, we have seen a shift away from eating fresh, whole, natural plant and animal foods, to a diet now dominant in highly processed man-made foods. Along with a processed diet there has been an increase in chronic degenerative 'lifestyle' diseases, breathing disorders and mental health conditions. These diseases and disorders are also showing up at younger ages.

For some people, dietary changes are so important that it's vital they are made first before there can be much progress in natural control of breathing and anxiety. What you learn here may enhance your results in an extraordinary way.

Note: This information is not a diet or a full nutrition plan. You need to consider it in relation to any medical conditions you may have and your own dietary needs. I advise you to educate yourself widely on this topic and if appropriate, discuss this information with your doctor or nutritionist before making any changes.

When I see clients with anxiety, I often suggest some dietary adjustments at our initial or second appointment. I base this decision on the information contained in the two-day food diary – see below – and what I learn from their history, breathing pattern and symptom assessments. I suggest you fill it in now.

TWO-DAY FOOD DIARY

Instructions A: Grab a pen and a highlighter. With the pen, write in the table below everything you ate in the last two days, or for two typical days. Include drinks, sugar in tea and coffee, each food that made up your meal, and what was on your toast and sandwich. (This table is also in the downloadable workbook – see Learning Resources page 201.)

TABLE 9.1: MEAL COMPONENTS

MEAL	YESTERDAY	TODAY
Breakfast		
Morning tea		
Lunch		
Afternoon tea		
Dinner		

Instructions B: Using the highlighter, mark all foods that contain high-sugar/high-starch carbohydrates. Food:

- that contains added sugar (e.g. soft drink, sweets, cake, jam), and/or
- with high natural sugar content (e.g. fruit juice, fruit, dried fruit), or
- high in starch (e.g. potato, fries, corn, rice, pasta, breakfast cereal, cake, bread).

HOW BALANCED ARE YOUR MEALS?

Now, look at how much of these foods you ate in each meal or snack, compared to foods containing protein, fat and low-sugar/low-starch carbohydrates (most vegetables).

- Is your diet skewed towards high-sugar/high-starch carbohydrates foods? ___
- Are there some meals and snacks that contain only these foods? ___
- Notice how you feel after a typical meal:
- After lunch does your nose block up?___
- If yes, what did you have for lunch? ______________________________
- Do you feel 'foggy', anxious, agitated, or bloated, but hungry again about an hour after eating? ___
- If yes, what did you eat? ______________________________
- Do you feel tired or sleepy after a high sugar/ high starch meal? ___
- If you have a disturbed sleep some nights, are there any particular foods usually involved? ______________________________

Many years of observing this among people with anxiety and other breathing-related disorders has shown me that there is a pattern. Agitation, anxiety, racing heart, congestion, breathlessness, low energy, and brain fog are more likely to follow meals and snacks dominated by high-sugar/high-starch carbohydrates like cereals, pasta, rice, bread, potatoes, pastries, and baked goods.

You are about to learn why, along with some very simple and satisfying food adjustments you can make in order to breathe and feel better.

'STRESSFUL' FOODS

Foods I classify as 'stressful' are those that put stress on your body, and on your breathing, as you digest them. Some foods are stressful because of what *is* in them, e.g. high-sugar/high-starch foods and additive-laden processed foods. Others are stressful because of what's *not* in them, e.g. nutrient-deficient foods.

Foods that cause a spike in blood sugar

The first category of stressful foods causes a spike in blood-sugar level. Stable blood sugar is a cornerstone of health. Abnormal blood-sugar levels are linked to diabetes and weight problems. Fluctuations in blood sugar have also been linked to anxiety and mood disorder. Let's look at the sugar–breathing–mind connection.

SNEAKY SUGAR AND LOW-FAT FOODS

The average daily consumption of added sugars in the western diet is about 22 teaspoons. We know about the spoonful in our coffee, but the sneaky sources include soft drinks, cereals, flavoured milk and yoghurts, spreads, sauces, and the trendy 'low-fat' foods. Manufacturers add sugar to boost the flavour of so-called healthy low-fat products which would otherwise taste like cardboard. Of the 600,000 items in the American food supply, 80 per cent are laced with added sugar.[9.1] Sugar is known by at least 30 different names.

Sugar is the number one food enemy to breathing. We get our daily sugar load from more than just added sugar in processed foods. All carbohydrate foods ultimately break down to glucose, a simple sugar that is absorbed into the bloodstream. Foods that are mainly carbohydrate include sugar, fruit, non-starchy vegetables (e.g. green vegetables, salad vegetables), starchy vegetables (e.g. potatoes, corn), and grains (e.g. wheat, rice, oats, rye). The rate at which the carbohydrate content of these foods converts to sugar and enters the bloodstream varies. It also depends on the ratio of carbohydrate to protein and fat in a given meal or snack.

Today we can choose a wide variety of cuisines, which is fabulous...in one way. But it's also led to a huge surge in the popularity and consumption of energy-dense foods such as rice, pasta and noodle-based dishes, with serving portions and frequency of consumption often far exceeding those of the traditional cultures who consume them.

Blood sugar fluctuations and over-breathing are intimately connected. A meal or snack overabundant in sugary and starchy carbohydrates, especially refined ones (white sugar, high-fructose corn syrup, white flour, white rice, instant oats) and the products made from them (breakfast cereals, breads, pasta, risotto, biscuits, pies, cakes, desserts, ice-cream, soft drinks), can result in a rapid rise in blood sugar because far more sugar is released into the bloodstream than is needed for energy.

This causes the pancreas to release insulin, whose job is to remove sugar from the bloodstream. If during this process the blood-sugar level falls too

quickly or becomes too low, the adrenal glands are stimulated and adrenaline is released. With an increase in adrenaline comes an increase in breathing rate. You have the fight-or-flight response.

Symptoms may include feeling dizzy, shaky, agitated, or anxious. Hunger and cravings for the type of carbohydrates that spike blood sugar can follow, with a rollercoaster ride of fluctuating blood-sugar levels and an assortment of symptoms. It's no secret that consuming sugar will get you wired, at least initially. Many people get tired, sleepy or moody an hour or so after a high-sugar/high-starch meal.

Unfortunately, many of the comfort foods anxious people use such as alcohol, biscuits, bread, pasta, and sweets contribute to their problem.

What comfort foods do you eat that are sugar-spiking? ______________

____

Some people have a strong reaction to a high-starch/high-sugar meal; others may just feel below par with a vague sense of unease or fatigue. Although the release of adrenaline is your body's natural response to maintain equilibrium, your adrenal glands have to enact this emergency procedure every time you eat a lot of blood-sugar raising foods. This is very stressful to your adrenals, your breathing and your body as a whole.

What percentage of your meals in Table 9.1 was dominant in sugar-spiking foods? ____

THROWING FAT ON THE FIRE

Swings in blood sugar, and therefore in breathing, are moderated when you eat sufficient protein foods with naturally occurring fat in the same meal as carbohydrates. An example would be a roasted chicken breast (with the skin on), served with steamed carrots, broccoli and a potato dressed with olive oil or sour cream. Protein and fat are digested more slowly. They slow down the release of sugar into the blood, avoiding the quick changes in blood-sugar levels that lead to over-breathing. They also provide valuable nutrients to make you feel full sooner and for longer, and they provide longer-lasting energy.

In the modern diet, protein foods with their naturally occurring healthy fats are often low in comparison to starch-rich, sugar-rich carbohydrates. Protein with naturally occurring fat is found in meat, fish, chicken, cheese, and eggs, also in nuts, seeds and avocados. How many of your meals in Table 9.1 had little to no protein and fat? ____

Rose treated herself to lunch in a cafe while she read her novel. The tuna salad was a generous size, but there was very little tuna in it. Deciding to linger over her book, Rose ordered the delicious looking carrot cake. It was a big slice and before she finished it, she started to feel unsettled, agitated and spacey and could no longer concentrate on her book. Rose quickly paid the bill and left the cafe. Almost on auto-pilot, she went to the corner store and bought a packet of cashews. Halfway through them she felt fine again.

Rose had remembered to 'put fat on the fire', that is, to dampen an out-of-control blood-sugar 'fire' with a food high in protein and/or fat. Her lunch was too heavily weighted in carbohydrate for her metabolism. There was very little protein and fat in her salad, and the carrot cake was a big hit of sugar.

Other options for dampening a blood-sugar surge are avocado, a hard-boiled egg and a chicken drumstick. Nuts are great (unless you are allergic of course), as they are easy to find and to carry with you.

From my observations of the diets of hundreds of anxiety sufferers, excess sugar and starchy sugar-forming foods may often be a factor in pushing them towards a chronic over-breathing and fight-or-flight state. Our bodies are simply not designed to process large amounts of sugar and refined grains.

Reducing sugar in the diet and getting some protein and healthy fat in each meal or snack has helped many stabilise their breathing and calm and stabilise their mood.

One way of knowing whether you have the fat/protein/carbohydrate proportion right in your meal is because you feel satisfied for at least three hours after a meal, often as much as five hours.

Matthew was so embarrassed at his first appointment. He apologised profusely in case I could smell alcohol on his breath – it was only 9 am. "I'm not an alcoholic," he said, "I just couldn't have come here today without a small brandy first." Matthew suffered from agoraphobia and used brandy to relax him enough to tackle the anxiety associated with going somewhere out of his comfort zone. Matthew's over-breathing was as obvious to me as it had been to his new doctor who had referred him. However, I did not work with his breathing that first day. I quizzed him about his diet. In his typical day, he ate virtually no protein or fat in any meal or snack. Breakfast was toast and jam; snacks were sweet biscuits or crackers; lunch was a tomato sandwich; and dinner was pasta with a tomato-based sauce. I knew that he would need to stabilise his blood sugar first before he could ever hope to focus on his breathing. I found out what proteins and fats he liked and suggested some easy meal and snack substitutes and additions.

I phoned Matthew the next day. Already he felt so much better, calmer, steadier, and hopeful. Two days later he called to book himself in for breathing lessons, choosing classes over one-to-one sessions. That was a real breakthrough for an agoraphobic.

Inflammatory foods

Another category of stressful foods are those that may trigger an inflammatory response in the body. (An increased breathing rate is part of the inflammatory response.) The sugar-spiking foods discussed above fall in this category. So do refined, highly processed vegetable oils like sunflower, safflower and canola oil.

It is now suspected that these highly processed oils, and the partially hydrogenated vegetable oils and trans fats made from them, contribute to coronary heart disease (an inflammatory process) rather than protecting us from it. Such vegetable oils and trans fats are commonly used in fast-food, restaurant and home cooking, in margarines and dressings, and they are present in almost all processed foods and commercially baked goods including biscuits, pastries, cakes, crackers, breads, and some snack foods.

Your healthy gut bacteria, the microflora population, can be severely reduced by eating loads of sugars and processed foods. The void is filled by disease-causing bacteria, yeast and fungi that all promote inflammation.

VITAMIN D – NATURE'S PROZAC

Vitamin D deficiency has been associated with depression. Studies have found higher levels of depression in areas that receive less sunlight, and significantly lower blood levels of vitamin D in people with depression.

Nutrient deficient foods: low in minerals, fat, and fat-soluble vitamins

Deficiencies of nutrients are linked with anxiety and mood disorders. For example, the depletion of nutrient reserves during a pregnancy and a lack of recovery of those nutrient levels after the birth may increase a woman's risk of post-natal depression.

Today, much of our fruit, vegetable and grain crops are grown in soils lacking in many essential minerals and trace elements. Further nutrients are lost during storage, transportation and commercial processing. Many of the animals that provide a source of primary protein, nutrient-dense fats and other concentrated nutrients are often not reared on their natural food sources, and this changes the quantity and quality of nutrients available. For example, red meat is normally a concentrated source of minerals because the animals spend their lives on pasture, chomping down masses of green grass and other plant matter. Today, however, cattle may spend their lives in feedlots and be grain-fed.

HEALTHY FATS

Foods high in vitamins A and D, omega-3s and other essential fatty acids include butter, whole goat and cow milk, fat on meat from grass-fed animals, egg yolks from pastured chickens, cod-liver oil and wild-caught fish. Omega-3s are also abundant in certain nuts and seeds such as flaxseeds and walnuts. Other healthy fats include avocado, coconut and coconut oil, olive oil, and unheated organic nut oils.

Grass-fed meats, free-range eggs and 'wild caught' oily fish have higher amounts of the valuable omega-3 fatty acids compared to the produce of their feedlot, caged and farmed counterparts. The eggs of pastured chickens have been found to have anywhere from 2–20 times the amount of omega-3s as commercial eggs.

When our diet is deficient in natural animal fats, we also miss out on the fat-soluble vitamins (A, D, E and K) they contain. It is very hard to get adequate amounts of these vitamins from plant foods. These vitamins are important in skeletal development, prevention of tooth decay, immunity, and the health of our nervous system.

It is increasingly recognised that fats and fatty acids are beneficial to brain function and general and mental health. Yes, you heard right! Healthy, natural fat is good! Not just good, but essential.

And that includes the much-maligned saturated fats. A recent multi-study review concluded that current evidence does *not* support encouraging low consumption of saturated fat for heart health.[9.2]

We need fats to produce neurotransmitters and hormones.

FATS, LIPIDS AND YOUR MENTAL HEALTH

Fats offer far more than the much-touted cardiovascular benefits of omega-3 fats. The fat-soluble vitamins and fatty acids they contain play an important role in preventing mental illness and in maintaining emotional health.

Dopamine, serotonin, cortisol, brain function

Fatty acids cooperate with the fat-soluble vitamins A and D to regulate the adrenal hormone cortisol, which is responsible for the fight-or-flight response, and the neurotransmitter dopamine, which is responsible for motivation. Nutrient-rich animal fats therefore play a role in preventing anxiety, nervous tension and feelings of self-defeat. They are necessary for physical, social, mental, and emotional health.

Omega-3 fats are also known to affect our serotonin levels and they are anti-inflammatory. People with a diet rich in omega-3s are less likely to suffer from anxiety, depression, schizophrenia, attention-deficit hyperactivity disorder (ADHD), or Alzheimer's disease.[9.3]

Fat and hormones

Fats are used to make hormones. Steroid hormones such as cortisol, progesterone, oestrogen, and testosterone are derived from cholesterol. We need to have some fat with every meal to maintain a healthy hormonal system.

Feeding the brain and nerves

Saturated fats such as butter, meat fats and coconut oil are essential for the structural integrity and optimal function of our cell membranes and our nervous system. Over half the fat in the brain is saturated fat. The fat-soluble vitamins A and D are also needed for a healthy nervous system, along with many other things.

Cholesterol

Most people are worried about having high cholesterol levels. However, many are unaware that a low cholesterol level has actually been linked to poor brain function and memory loss,[9.4] aggressive behaviour and depression,[9.5] and depression and suicide.[9.6]

Cholesterol in the brain plays an important role in the release of brain neurotransmitters such as serotonin, so important for your emotional and mental health. According to Yeon-Kyun Shin, a biophysics professor from Iowa State University, studies indicate that cholesterol-lowering drugs (statins) may keep the

brain from making cholesterol, thereby affecting the release of neurotransmitters.[9.7.1] In addition, vitamin D, progesterone, oestrogen, testosterone, and cortisol are all derived from cholesterol.

Processed, artificial, chemical-laden and engineered 'foods'

Much of our food today is grown or produced and processed with artificial chemicals and additives. Our bodies have to work harder to digest and process unnatural foodstuffs and our breathing rate will increase as it does so.

Processed milk products

Processing milk greatly diminishes its nutritional value and makes it indigestible for many people. High-temperature *pasteurisation* not only kills any harmful bacteria but also destroys the beneficial bacteria and valuable enzymes that help us to digest milk. It also diminishes vitamin content, destroys vitamin B12 and alters the structure of fragile milk proteins. The *homogenisation* process denatures the butterfat globules. Commonly reported symptoms from consuming excess commercially processed milk include nasal and sinus congestion, mucus, asthma, and digestive upset. Pasteurised, homogenised milk from intensively farmed commercial herds is a very different product from the healthy staple of our forebears, which was raw milk from the house cow or local organic farmer.

Observe yourself to see what, if any, effects dairy products have on your breathing and how you feel. Work out what is appropriate consumption for you.

Poorly prepared foods

Grains, seeds and legumes need proper preparation to make them more digestible. Our healthy ancestors knew how to prepare foods for better digestion using soaking, sour leavening and fermenting. Modern food preparation often skips or shortens these important steps, sacrificing speed over quality nutrition and digestion. Your breathing may well feel the stress.

THE IMPORTANCE OF GOOD BACTERIA – TO YOUR GUT AND BRAIN

Properly fermented foods like sauerkraut and kefir supply your body with enzymes and friendly bacteria. These gut flora are essential for healthy gut and immune function. The lack of friendly bacteria due to poor diet, digestive illness or over-use of antibiotics is now thought to be a contributing cause of depression.[9.8] This is logical. The greatest concentration of the mood hormone serotonin is found in your intestines, not your brain. For optimum serotonin function, you need the correct balance of healthy gut flora as well as balanced breathing. Nothing in your body works in isolation!

Caffeine foods: coffee, tea, cola, chocolate

Foods containing caffeine stimulate your adrenal glands and cause dopamine levels to rise. Breathing rate increases too. That's why a double shot of espresso can make you alert and euphoric, as well as possibly jittery and anxious. In excess, caffeine is detrimental to your adrenal glands, good breathing and quality sleep.

Alcohol

Alcohol can at first be an 'upper' for your mood, giving you a feeling of general relaxation. But later, as the alcohol is metabolised, breathing increases. With that can come snoring, headache, agitation, and/or nausea. Alcohol is also a 'downer' – it can be followed by low mood the next day.

We will now have a brief look at some other interconnections between eating and breathing.

BREATHING AFFECTS DIGESTION

In Chapters 6 and 7, we looked at the many ways that incorrect breathing can negatively affect various body systems. In the gastrointestinal system, it affects the blood supply, nerve supply and muscular activity of the gut wall.

Over-breathing/low carbon dioxide reduces the blood supply to the gastrointestinal tract, compromising the process of digestion and the ability to extract nutrients from food. It also results in spasm and abnormal function of the smooth muscle in the wall of the gut. The consequences may include heartburn, colic, irritable bowel, belching, bloating, diarrhoea, constipation, and flatulence. Many people notice improvements in gut function within 24 to 48 hours of starting breathing retraining. Commonly reported benefits include:

- reduced constipation and flatulence
- reduction in colic and irritable bowel symptoms
- reduced heartburn
- reduction in excess appetite
- fewer cravings for processed and sugary food
- more stable blood-sugar level
- easier weight normalisation
- increased energy, exercise capacity and endurance.

Have you noticed any of these changes since you have been working on breathing more gently and through your nose?

HOW WE EAT IS IMPORTANT TOO

There are four simple principles to follow to help your breathing and digestion.

Eat when you are hungry

Hunger is a physiological sign that your body is in need of nutrients and ready to receive and digest food. Eating when you are not hungry – because you are emotional, bored, there is still food on the plate, have cravings, or just 'because it's morning tea time' – can cause considerable stress to your body and increase your breathing rate. Of course, sharing meals with family and friends is an important social activity. By getting to know your body well, you can eventually time your natural hunger to fit in with planned meal times.

Stop when you have had enough

It is estimated that we now eat between two and three times more than we did 50 years ago, and we get far less exercise. Overeating puts stress on your body and deepens your breathing – you now know what trouble that can get you into. If overeating also results in becoming overweight, the extra weight you carry requires more effort and therefore more breathing for you to move around. Life becomes so much harder than it needs to be.

Many people notice that as their breathing improves, they require less food to satisfy their hunger and energy needs and they have more energy.

Overall, they usually feel better, find it easier to exercise and can more easily shed excess weight. For the sake of your breathing and your health, tune in, eat only when hungry and stop when you've had enough.

Eat slowly, chew well; don't gulp air

Eating quickly and gulping air in can lead to shortness of breath, noisy eating and wind problems. To avoid this, don't breathe in while you are putting food (or liquids) into your mouth. Once the food is in, close your mouth and try to breathe through your nose while you chew and swallow. This usually results in taking smaller mouthfuls, eating and drinking more slowly and chewing more thoroughly. It also gives your body a chance to recognise when you have had enough.

Allow two hours between evening meal and bedtime

Increased breathing happens naturally during digestion. If you have baseline over-breathing and you are still digesting when you go to bed, your breathing volume will increase further, making it even more likely you will have insomnia or snore. Allow two hours for digestion after a meal; three hours if it's a heavy meal.

INDIVIDUAL DIFFERENCES: GETTING HELP

Try to identify the foods and food combinations that worsen your breathing and your anxiety levels. Keeping a food diary may help. If you have a medicated blood-sugar disorder, it is very important to work with a proficient nutritional therapist.

HEALTHY PEOPLE – TRADITIONAL EATING

Today, our hospitals and doctors' waiting rooms are full of people with poor nutrition. Rarely is it diagnosed. They are also full of people who have dysfunctional breathing – also rarely diagnosed. So what should we eat? Who and what should we believe?

With powerful advertising campaigns for addictively tasty, highly processed foods and conflicting advice from dieticians, it is difficult to know. I don't claim to be an expert. However, as with breathing, the concept of staying with what is natural for the human body resonates with me. We are designed to breathe 4–6 litres of air per minute; we are designed to eat a selection of clean, fresh, whole, natural plant and animal foods. We would do well to return to the principles of nature-based diets of 'traditional' populations who had little chronic disease and often lived to over 100 years of age. If it costs more to eat well, isn't it better to pay a little more to the grocer and less to the doctor?

Back to the future

Your great-grandparents were much less likely than you are to have an anxiety disorder, mental illness, sleep apnoea, be obese, or suffer from asthma, diabetes, irritable bowel syndrome, or cancer. If they were like mine (born in the mid-1800s), they ate fruit and vegetables in season and a variety of whole grains. They drank the milk and ate the meat of pasture-raised animals that lived a peaceful existence; they ate the eggs and meat of chickens that wandered about the yard indulging in their natural pickings. They ate real butter on fermented sourdough bread. They did not get fat or have heart attacks from eating natural unprocessed fat. My great-grandparents lived a healthy life into their 80s without chronic illness.

While we wait for definitive answers regarding the many nutritional controversies that plague our times, we can learn from our ancestors. You could ask yourself, "Would my great-grandmother recognise this as food?"

By restoring balance to your diet, you are likely to notice a reduction in breathing-related symptoms. Great-grandmother had the right idea with her meat and three vegetables meals.

We may not be able to change our genes or some aspects of our life circumstances, but we can choose to eat well, we can choose to breathe well and we can teach our children well.

Note: The suggestions above are not based on total dietary requirements and may be unsuitable for some people with particular medical conditions and food requirements. Check with your doctor about your particular situation.

WATER, SALT AND BREATHING

Being sufficiently hydrated is important. The water in your body helps send chemicals and nutrients around the body and in and out of your cells. The amount of water you need depends on several factors, including your state of health, your level of physical activity and the climate. You need more fluids on a hot day and when involved in strenuous or sustained exercise in hot, dry conditions. In general, the more you sweat, the more you need to drink. The amount of water you need also depends on your diet and how you breathe.

Fat makes water

All foods contain water. Some foods are 'water-rich', such as lettuce, cucumber and watermelon. Unbeknown to many, the fat content of food is critical to cell hydration. Fats, especially saturated fats, make much more water during metabolism than do carbohydrates or proteins. When our diet is fat-deficient we can become dehydrated.[9.9]

Bad breathers lose lots of water

The more air you breathe, the more you need to drink. This is especially if you mouth breathe, as you miss out on the nose's humidifying ability.

Water, as water vapour, leaves with the gases from your lungs when you breathe out. Water loss is high in over-breathers. Breathing correctly, at five litres per minute, you will lose approximately 320 ml of water over a day. Breathe at 12–15 litres per minute and over the course of a day, you may lose up to a litre of water. When you reduce over-breathing, you soon experience a less dry mouth, less thirst and less sticky mucus. Your need for water will then be less.

Salt matters

Salt is also important in hydration and body function – the right amount of salt and the right type of salt. Natural, unrefined sea salts provide 80 or more trace elements and minerals essential for health. Trace minerals are required to make the electrolytes necessary for many cell functions, and to activate digestive enzymes. They are important in maintaining hydration, adrenal function and the body's electrical systems, like heart function and nerve transmission. Refined salt, often used in commercially processed foods and 'fast foods', is stripped of its natural mineral structure and is virtually all sodium.[9,10]

Salt is also known for its healing effects on mucus membranes (as in saline nasal washes, see Chapter 13). Natural sea salt has been found by some people to be helpful with headache, nasal congestion, dizziness, panic attacks, and fatigue. Dr Buteyko's recommendation for these is ¼ teaspoon or a pinch of natural unprocessed salt dissolved in a cup of warm water and sipped during a flare-up of these symptoms.

Note: If you are on a salt-restricted diet, check with your doctor before adjusting your salt intake.

IN SUMMARY

While the social, cognitive and spiritual factors that influence mental health are important, the physiological elements – those relating to how your body is functioning – must be attended to. Normalising body function through correct breathing and supply of necessary nutrients by eating whole, fresh, natural plant and animal foods, including animal fats with their fatty acids and fat-soluble vitamins, will help you avoid anxiety and mood disorders. Maintaining stable blood-sugar levels through balanced portions of protein, fat and carbohydrate in the diet is the other cornerstone to success in beating the anxiety cycle.

It is important to educate yourself about food. It is beyond the scope of this book to adequately cover nutrition in all its aspects. In Recommended Reading in Learning Resources page 203 you will find suggestions for further reading. Seek advice from a nutritionist if you have diabetes or other blood-sugar disorders, and if your diet or digestive processes have been inadequate for quite some time.

ACTION STEPS FOR HEALTHY EATING

- Eat only when you are hungry; stop when satisfied.
- Maintain an appropriate weight.
- Sit down and slow down when eating.

- Allow 2–3 hours between eating and before going to bed
- Eat a balance of protein, natural fat and carbohydrate at every meal and snack.

Avoid: processed, highly-refined, high-salt, high-sugar/high-starch, additive and preservative laden, chemically treated and modified foods, including packaged cereals and commercially baked goods, soft drinks and low-fat manipulated dairy.

Favour: fresh, local, organic, nutritious whole foods, including wild or ethically raised fish, pastured poultry and meats, fruits and vegetables, nuts and seeds, some legumes, fermented vegetables and cultured dairy, and grains that are properly prepared (e.g. sourdough). Favour foods your great-grandmother would recognise.

Balance: Eat adequate protein and fat at each meal or snack; eat a variety of vegetables; limit starchy carbohydrates such as rice, pasta and other grain foods; maintain a healthy gut flora by including naturally fermented foods in your diet.

Suggestions

Breakfast. Full-fat yoghurt with fruit and nuts; omelette (eggs, shallots, parsley, avocado, tomato) and one slice of buttered sourdough toast.

Lunch and dinner. Fish and steamed vegetables sprinkled with sea salt, butter or olive oil, side of sauerkraut; steak and vegetable casserole with a side of rice and sauerkraut.

Snacks. Piece of fruit and a small handful of nuts; cheese and celery sticks; hummus and carrot sticks; a hard-boiled egg and a small apple.

You've now completed Part One of the book. Hopefully, you have a good understanding of the physiology behind anxiety and stress-related conditions and your experience of them.

Part Two is about how to change your breathing, day by day and habit by habit, building on the benefits of healthy breathing that you have already started.

You can now look forward to further improvement in your health and your quality of life.

PART TWO

HOW TO CHANGE YOUR BREATHING: DAY BY DAY, HABIT BY HABIT

'Everyone thinks of changing the world, but no one thinks of changing himself.'

LEO TOLSTOY

CHAPTER 10

The breathing retraining approach

This chapter gives an outline of the key concepts behind breathing retraining and describes the process and typical results seen. The remaining chapters are then devoted to getting your breathing right.

KEY CONCEPTS

Abnormal breathing patterns are characteristic of people with anxiety disorders

The connection between dysfunctional breathing and anxiety disorders is well established.[10.1 - 10.3] Research shows patients with panic disorder have chronic over-breathing, with faster breathing, larger amounts of air consumed and significantly lower carbon dioxide levels than normal[10.4, 10.5] as well as more irregular, 'chaotic' and unstable breathing.

The aim is to normalise the breathing pattern

The primary goal of breathing retraining is to normalise the breathing pattern. The intent is to *retrain* (that is, recondition or reset) your *respiratory centre*, the part of your brain that regulates your breathing, to operate at the correct level.

By normalising your breathing, you can:

- normalise your blood chemistry
- prevent or sedate the fight-or-flight response
- enhance oxygen delivery to every cell in your body
- bring stability and normality to the way your body functions.

Breathing is 're-trainable' – habits can be changed

Think of the respiratory centre in your brain as having a manual override and reset button. If the carbon dioxide receptors there can become accustomed to high volume breathing and low carbon dioxide levels, so too can they get re-accustomed to normal (lower) breathing volumes and normal carbon dioxide levels. The respiratory centre has *plasticity*. This means it can be retrained.

BREATHING RETRAINING VS. OTHER FORMS OF BREATH WORK

Breathing retraining in this book is often very different from breath work and breathing exercises taught in other disciplines such as physiotherapy, speech pathology, psychology, singing, yoga, Pilates, and fitness training.

DEFINITION OF BREATHING RETRAINING

Breathing retraining is the specific discipline in which the primary goal is to normalise each aspect of the breathing pattern (rate, rhythm, volume, mechanics, use of the nose), for all situations (awake, asleep, at rest, during eating, speech and exercise).

This definition makes breathing retraining very different from therapeutic or 'special purpose' breathing exercises that you might do in hospital, in meditation, yoga or Pilates classes, or using various breathing devices. These may have particular aims such as clearing mucus, filling and expanding the bases of the lungs, relaxation, 'centring the mind', 'strengthening the core', or strengthening breathing muscles.

Other disciplines may promote some aspects of normal breathing, for example, slow diaphragm breathing, but may also encourage large tidal volumes, exhaling through the mouth and emptying the lungs. Instructions might include 'take big deep breaths', 'fill your lungs', 'breathe out as far as you can'.

When the emphasis is on breathing a lot of air in, breathing out fully and wanting to see the lower abdomen moving in and out, the practice is *not* about restoring a normal breathing pattern. It may involve considerable hyperventilation. While yoga and Pilates are well recognised for their positive effects on wellbeing, for someone who has dysfunctional baseline breathing, the practice of full, deep (belly) breaths may bring on light-headedness, anxiety or a panic attack.

Be careful when choosing a breathing instructor if your aim is to breathe normally, which for most people means breathing considerably *less* air! Proper breathing retraining does not make you dizzy, short of breath, panicky, or fatigued.

WHO TEACHES BREATHING RETRAINING?

Breathing retraining as a separate discipline is still relatively new and the number of teachers and breathing educators is small but growing. They come from various backgrounds; in my case, it was physiotherapy (see also Chapter 26). The style of breathing retraining I teach – *BreatheAbility* – is not physically demanding, uncomfortable or challenging. You can practise while sitting, standing and walking, blending better breathing practice into normal daily activities.

THE BREATHING RETRAINING PROCESS

A typical program with a breathing educator involves an initial consultation, then a structured program of between five and seven additional sessions. It is often ideal to do the first five sessions within a 10-day period.

The components of the breathing retraining process are:

- assessment
- education
- practical instruction.

Assessment identifies abnormal breathing habits, symptoms and triggers. It looks at breathing mechanics, use of the breathing muscles and breathing rhythm.

Education includes some basic anatomy and physiology to give an understanding of the breathing process and how it affects the way different body systems function. Behaviours and lifestyle factors that influence breathing are covered.

Practical components include breathing retraining exercises and techniques to:

- reduce nasal stuffiness, irritable cough, shortness of breath, and feelings of panic
- establish gentle, rhythmic, diaphragm breathing
- recondition the set point of breathing to make a healthy breathing pattern permanent, day and night, and prevent symptoms in the long term.

Breathing retraining also provides a foundation for fitness activities.

Medical reappraisal

When you undergo breathing retraining, it is advisable to see your doctor for reappraisal of your condition generally, and in particular when you notice significant change in your breathing pattern and symptoms. Changes in prescribed medication and treatments must be undertaken only in consultation with your doctor (see Chapter 24).

BENEFITS OF BREATHING RETRAINING

Getting your breathing right improves oxygenation to every cell in your body, balances your body chemistry and calms your nervous system. Many symptoms associated with breathing pattern dysfunction can resolve. The reasons for this are explained in Chapters 6 and 7.

The changes and benefits listed below typify those reported by clients, their family members, doctors and other healthcare professionals, and from 'before and after' scans, tests and sleep studies.

- less anxiety and tension
- improved focus and concentration
- better handling of stress
- deep feeling of calm/relaxation
- ability to nose breathe
- less mucus and congestion
- refreshing, quality sleep
- quieter, more regular breathing during sleep
- less or no snoring
- less waking and sleep disturbance
- fewer overnight toilet trips

- reduced leg twitching/restless legs
- less mouth and throat dryness
- greater muscle and general relaxation
- fewer headaches
- easier breathing at rest, during sleep and exercise
- more stamina and capacity, and faster recovery with exercise
- decline in asthma and sinus symptoms
- fewer colds.

THE BUTEYKO METHOD OF BREATHING RETRAINING

The Buteyko method of breathing retraining, developed in the 1950s by Ukrainian-born physician Konstantin Buteyko, is based on his decades of clinical practice and research using sophisticated equipment. I studied with and have been accredited by Professor Buteyko, and the Buteyko method has formed a substantial part of my clinical work. It was brought to Australia in 1990 and since then has been introduced into many countries.

How soon does it work?

Many people respond in the first session. Your stuffy nose usually improves within minutes. You may feel calmer and more in control within an hour of making the first gentle changes. You may sleep better right from the first night. My records show that five days into breathing retraining, most people have reduced their total symptom score by over 60 per cent.

The figures in Table 10.1 and Table 10.2 below are taken from my records. They are typical for adults attending programs, where the first five sessions are done on consecutive days. Some participants used the special Buteyko breathing techniques, others did not.

TABLE 10.1: RESPIRATION AND HEART RATES

	DAY 1	DAY 5
Average resting respiration rate	16	11
Average resting heart rate	78	63

TABLE 10.2: SYMPTOM SCORE REDUCTIONS

	DAY 5	FOLLOW-ON SESSION (APPROX. DAY 10)
Average reduction in Symptom Score	60–69 %	73–82 %

WORKING WITH OTHER THERAPIES

If you have a mental health crisis, you need pharmaceutical and psychological support straightaway. A combination approach is best, as it involves an active approach to the problem and the opportunity to learn more ways to cope, rather than the passive 'I took a pill and it made me better'.

One of the difficulties with counselling or cognitive behavioural therapy is that it can take a lot of time and discipline, compared to taking medication which is often a 'quick fix'. This can be an obstacle if you lack motivation or feel overwhelmed.

Two of the best things about breathing retraining are:

- the changes can be blended into your everyday life
- you usually feel the benefits within 24 hours.

If you are undergoing counselling or psychological therapy, having your breathing and therefore your physiology attended to early on means you will probably achieve faster, deeper and more stable results from therapy. Your stress response will be quietened, and you will be able to think more creatively and be more realistic, when your baseline over-breathing is addressed. Psychologists are among the most consistent and enthusiastic referrers to our breathing clinic.

Now let me give you the tools that thousands of my clients have found effective for improving their breathing, calming them, boosting their energy, and restoring restful sleep.

CHAPTER 11

The program: Nine healthy habits in nine days

It's time now to develop all the good breathing habits you have been reading about and learn how to apply them in your daily life. You are likely well on your way to establishing healthy breathing habits one and two: Awareness (Chapter 12) and Nose breathing (Chapter 13).

The aim of this program is to get you to breathe quietly, gently and rhythmically, day and night (see Figure 11.1 below). Figure 11.2 shows the nine healthy breathing habits.

FIGURE 11.1: THE AIM OF THE NINE-DAY PROGRAM

OUR AIM IS TO CHANGE THIS:

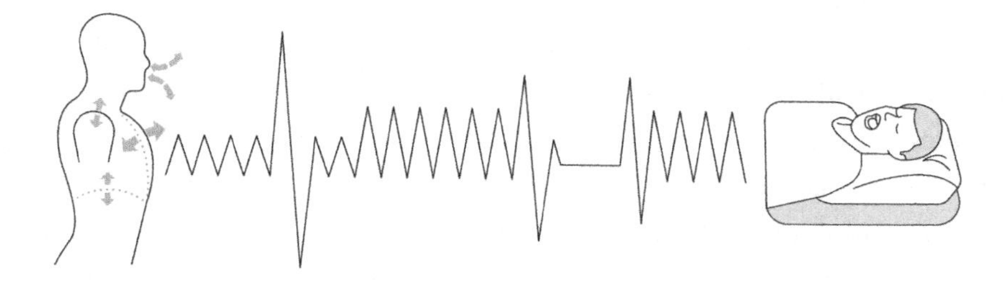

INTO THIS:

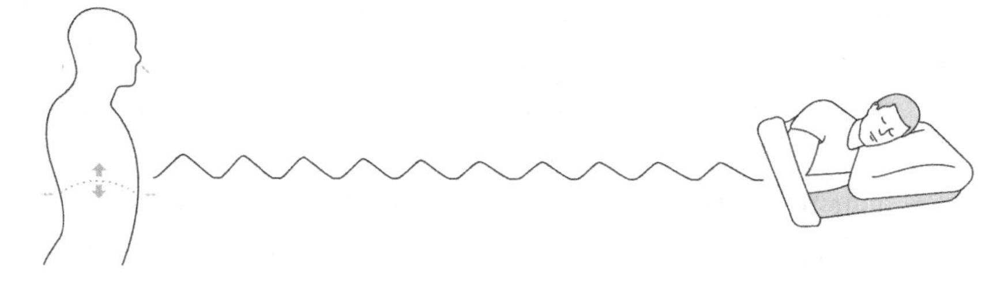

FIGURE 11.2: THE NINE HEALTHY BREATHING HABITS

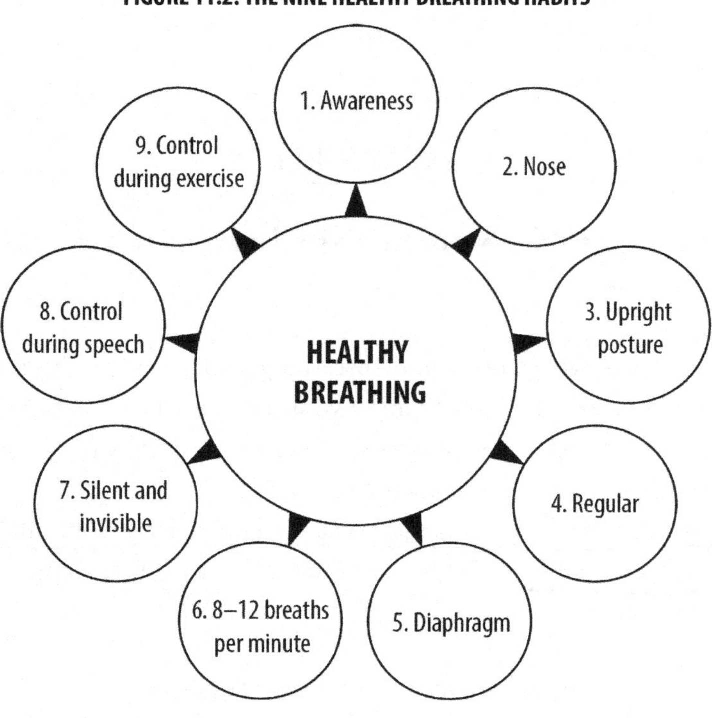

NINE-DAY PROGRAM TO BETTER BREATHING

You can learn and implement these healthy breathing habits in as little as nine days, with as little 'formal', that is, designated practice of just 5–10 minutes a few times a day. With familiarity, much of your practice can be informal, that is, blended into your normal activities. In fact, that is the best way. Like speaking a different language, becoming a better breather is best done regularly in everyday situations until it becomes a consistent, natural habit. In an astonishingly short time, a lifetime of harmful breathing habits can be transformed. How good is that?

Most people can make great progress by following the program in Table 11.1 below. That is not to say everyone will have perfect breathing by day nine, but it should be significantly improved and your symptoms significantly fewer. Nine days into breathing retraining it is usual to see a greater than 70% reduction in total symptom score. After that, you need to continue healthy breathing habits in everyday life, and further practise will help you achieve the best breathing pattern possible and it becomes second nature.

Some people need more days at each stage, especially if they have complicating factors such as serious illness or an acute illness at the time, like a cold. The level of improvement also depends on what posture you start out with, your diet and any medications you may take.

The best sequence to work through is the order the habits are given in. However, there are suggestions for changing the order if you struggle with a particular habit. As you introduce new habits, you continue those from the previous day.

TABLE 11.1: THE TYPICAL NINE-DAY PROGRAM

TIME SPENT	HABITS	TICK WHEN LEARNT
Days 1 & 2	Awareness Nose breathing	
Day 3	Posture	
Day 4	Regular breathing	
Days 5 & 6	Diaphragm breathing	
Day 7	Silent, 'invisible' breathing	
Day 8	Breathing control during speech	
Day 9	Breathing well during exercise	

Healthy Habit Six (see Figure 11.2 – breathing 8–12 breaths a minute) is not included in this program guide because it doesn't have to be practised. It normally develops naturally from implementing the other habits. So that's one less thing to do.

Read through all the information in each section. Even if you see the heading and think 'I'm right with nose breathing/posture/diaphragm breathing', please read it anyway to be absolutely sure. Why? Because unconscious mouth breathing, especially during activity, is very common. Your idea of good posture may not match mine, and many people practise diaphragm breathing, but it is often woefully incorrect.

Address all nine habits for the sake of long-term and lasting benefits, not only for your anxiety condition, but also for general health. Breathing correctly will give you a wonderful tool to withstand the stresses of modern living. Think of it as a form of health insurance.

Symptom relief and rescue breathing exercises

You are given strategies for relief of common symptoms in each of the nine following chapters. Chapter 22 page 160 is devoted to quick-relief breathing exercises to control anxiety or panic attacks. Jump ahead there if you need to.

Tweak a little; change a lot

Overwhelm is easy for the anxious. I do not want you to feel overwhelmed. The preference is towards 'underwhelm'. Making tiny adjustments to your breathing each day can transform your life.

The wonderful thing about changing your breathing is that you have around 20,000 opportunities a day to make a difference. You don't have to stop other parts of your life to find time to take care of it. Simply take your next breath...differently.

Remember:

- You may need to check with your doctor before beginning breathing retraining.
- Read each section and implement the changes and action steps – at your pace.
- Move on to the next section when the previous habit is second nature, or when the instructions guide you to do so.
- Seek help from a breathing educator (see page 177) if you struggle to instil the correct habits.
- Stop implementing a new breathing habit if you experience any discomfort. Follow the suggestions given and seek guidance from a doctor and breathing educator if necessary.
- See your doctor for reassessment of any anxiety or sleep-breathing condition before discontinuing or changing any prescribed treatments (see Chapter 24).

CHAPTER 12

Healthy habit one: Awareness

WATCH YOUR BREATHING

The first step in improving your breathing is to be aware of the way you breathe and how it compares to normal, healthy breathing, which is nasal, smooth, satisfying, silent, small, slow, and relatively still. You have to notice your breathing faults before you can work on undoing them. Without this connection, you will struggle to make the changes.

Back in Chapters 1 and 3 you went through the self-assessment process. Now is a good time to look again at what you wrote down in Table 1.1. You are probably already much more aware of your breathing and you may have already made some changes, breathing more gently and doing less mouth breathing. However, when you put this book down and go about your business, without some level of mindfulness you may still revert to bad habits. When you get stressed, for example, you may notice your breathing gets faster and higher in your chest.

Many people think they are completely nose breathing during the daytime until they pay close attention. Then they discover they breathe through their mouth when walking, showering, concentrating, pegging out the washing, getting up from a chair, and getting in and out of the car.

OBSERVATION CHECKLIST

Tune in to the rate, rhythm, sound, route (mouth or nose), and location of your breathing. An 'all-the-time' general awareness is best, but to help you achieve this, I suggest you schedule a formal spot-check once every waking hour for two days.

Watch out for the particular breathing 'faults' in the left-hand column of

Table 12.1. Place an 'x' in each box where you notice these occurring in a certain situation. I suggest you carry this book or a photocopy of that page with you for the next few days – until you feel it is second nature to be aware of your breathing. This checklist is also in the downloadable workbook: BreatheAbility.com/store/.

TABLE 12.1: OBSERVATIONS CHECKLIST

HOW AM I BREATHING?	SITTING	MOVING ABOUT	UNDER STRESS	GETTING IN/OUT OF A CAR	LYING DOWN	ON WAKING	SHOWERING
Mouth							
Audible							
Fast							
Irregular							
Upper chest							
Breath holding							
Sighing							
Yawning							
Large, full breaths							
Coughing							
Sneezing							
Throat clearing							
Puffing/Panting							
Gasping when talking							

GETTING FEEDBACK

This can be very useful. You may have no idea how often you breathe through your mouth, clear your throat, sigh, yawn, sniff, or cough. These unconscious habits can, however, be quite obvious or even annoying to others.

> *William only became aware of his habitual cough when he overheard a work colleague identifying him to a new staff member as 'the guy in the cubicle over there who's always coughing'.*

Engage the help of family and friends. Explain that you want to be made aware so you can eliminate these habits. (They will probably be thrilled to help.) Give them permission to tell you when your mouth is open or your breathing is fast or noisy, until you're thoroughly aware of these habits. Ask your partner to observe your breathing during sleep. Even if you don't snore, your breathing may be audible, and you may be blowing a gale over your partner.

ACTION STEPS FOR BREATHING AWARENESS

- Generally watch your breathing throughout the day.
- Spot-check your breathing once an hour or so, for the first two days.
- Ask your family or friends to comment on your breathing.

When to move on

You can move on straightaway to Healthy Habit Two – Nose breathing – in the next chapter.

CHAPTER 13

Healthy habit two: Nose breathing

Work towards becoming a full-time nose breather, day and night, as well as with activity and exercise.

STRATEGIES FOR DAYTIME NOSE BREATHING

For many people, mouth breathing is a habit or it comes from a lack of awareness. Now that you are paying attention to the way you are breathing, and since Chapter 5 you have been 'shrinking your cloud' a little each day, you have probably made good progress with nose breathing. Even if nasal congestion has been a problem, it generally lessens as you reduce your tendency to mouth breathe and to over-breathe, thereby removing a source of inflammation to your mucous membranes. It usually doesn't take long before you feel a difference.

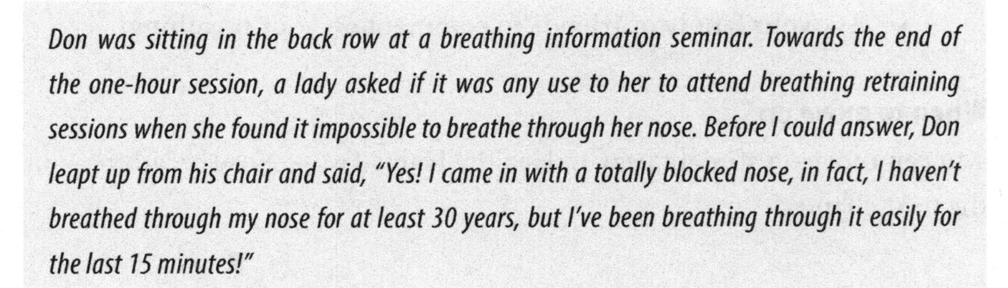

Don was sitting in the back row at a breathing information seminar. Towards the end of the one-hour session, a lady asked if it was any use to her to attend breathing retraining sessions when she found it impossible to breathe through her nose. Before I could answer, Don leapt up from his chair and said, "Yes! I came in with a totally blocked nose, in fact, I haven't breathed through my nose for at least 30 years, but I've been breathing through it easily for the last 15 minutes!"

Instructions

The following will help you become a consistent nose breather. If you are sure you are a consistent nose breather at all times, including during sleep, activity and light exercise, then move on to Chapter 14.

If the only time that you mouth breathe is during sleep, then turn to page 101 Strategies for nose breathing during sleep.

If you breathe through your nose at rest – sitting, at your desk, reading, standing – but not when you are active and walking around, including going up stairs, then start with Practice Set C below on page 100.

If your nose is *not* blocked but you are still mouth breathing after trying the preliminary instructions in Chapter 5 for two days, start with Practice Set A. Practice Set B is for those who have a blocked or congested nose.

PRACTICE SET A: NOSE BREATHING UNCOMFORTABLE BUT NOSE NOT BLOCKED

1. Determine how long you can maintain nose breathing before needing to take a breath (not a gasp) through your mouth. Let's say, for example, 15 seconds.
2. Go back to very gentle mouth breathing for 30 seconds.
3. Nose breathe again and try to add an extra 5–10 seconds before reverting to gentle mouth breathing again for 30 seconds.
4. Repeat three more times or until five minutes is up.

Try to increase the time you nose breathe in each cycle: from 15 seconds to 20 seconds, 30 seconds, 35 seconds, 45 seconds. After five minutes, take a break for an hour or so and then do the routine again. When you can comfortably breathe for 60 seconds continuously through your nose, try cutting down, or out, the 30-second mouth breathing breaks until you can comfortably and continuously nose breathe for the whole five minutes. Hopefully you can then keep up nose breathing throughout your next activity.

Aim to do this conscious practice once every waking hour until you are converted to continuous nose breathing. You can practise while watching TV, standing in a queue, sitting in a waiting room or on the bus. If at any time you feel short of breath, distress or panic, take a break and try again later.

Variation: walk around

Some people find it easier to practise nose breathing while moving about – *slowly*. If you do not like sitting still for long, then try it this way:

Go through steps 1–4 above but walk slowly, gradually increasing the time you nose breathe (number of steps taken) before reverting to gentle mouth breathing as you continue to walk. Same rules – no gasping, no distress.

PRACTICE SET B: YOUR NOSE FEELS BLOCKED

Short breath hold and 3 x 3 exercise

If you feel as if little or no air goes in when you try to nose breathe, try a *short breath hold.* This is a technique where after a normal (not forced) exhalation, you pause your breath for a count of *three* (between two and three seconds) then breathe slowly and gently for three breaths. Then repeat the pattern. This sequence of short breath holds is known as the 3 x 3 exercise. The slight increase in carbon dioxide that occurs with the breath holds seems to soothe swollen nasal membrane tissue.

Each hold/pause should not be so long as to alter the breathing pattern after the pause. That is, the breaths afterwards must be gentle, or at least not bigger or deeper than before (see Figure 13.1 below). If you hold too long and stimulate increased breathing, you lose the beneficial effect of the slight rise in carbon dioxide.

1. After a natural out-breath, pause your breath for a count of three (two to three seconds).
2. Breathe – as *gently* as you can – through your nose if it's clear or your mouth if it's not.
3. Repeat the pause after every third out-breath.
4. Follow this routine for two to three minutes.

FIGURE 13.1: THE SHORT BREATH HOLD AND 3 X 3 EXERCISE

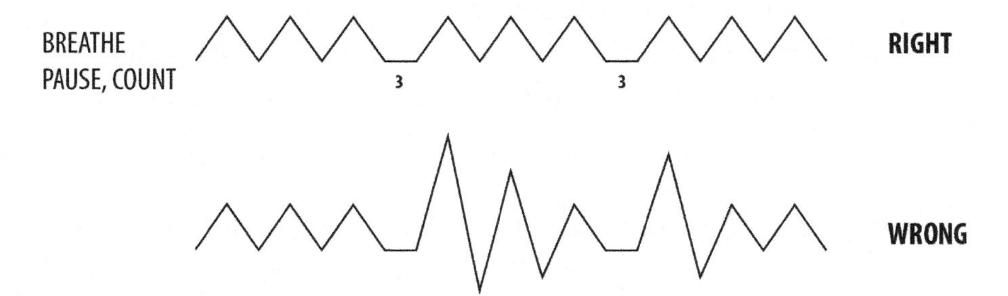

With the first few nose breaths, you may feel that not much air is getting through. Hopefully, your nose will gradually clear, with the nose breaths delivering an increasingly satisfying feeling. The gentler the nose and mouth breaths, the faster you should feel this effect.

Repeat Practice Set B once per waking hour if you can. When you find that your nose is no longer blocking up between practice times, you can try Practice Set A.

If at any stage during either set A or set B you feel distress, panic, breathlessness, or light-headedness, or you find yourself taking bigger mouth breaths, stop the practice, recover and breathe comfortably – however is comfortable for you. Take a break and come back later, or resume practice at the level of nose breathing time or short breath hold time you were comfortable with, and stay there until you feel ready to progress. It is very important that the nose breathing periods are *not* followed by deep breaths through your mouth. If they are, you have pushed yourself too far. Don't force the inhales or the exhales.

Also try nose breathing during movement. See Practice Set C below on page 100. By moving about slowly enough, you may even find it is easier than nose breathing while sitting.

Still mouth breathing? At least make it gentle

When you do have to mouth breathe, try to do it more gently, taking in less air than you used to. You will still be getting used to less air and becoming a more efficient breather. You may find you can be quite satisfied without sucking in as much air as you used to.

There are some additional strategies if needed on page 104 (Extra strategies for unblocking 'resistant' noses).

NOSE BREATHING DURING ACTIVITY AND MOVEMENT

Getting into the habit of nose breathing during light activity is very important. When you first switch from mouth breathing to nose breathing, this will most likely require you to walk and do day-to-day activities more slowly. Slow down to a pace at which you can *comfortably* nose breathe; don't push yourself into discomfort.

You may feel that you have to move at a snail's pace at first to achieve this, but it can make an incredible difference to your overall progress with improving your breathing. Allow yourself more time to get places – across the room, out to the garage, up the stairs, to your seat at the football, even more time to shower. The payoff is that you should be less breathless when you get there, and need less or no recovery time. Most people have their speed back within a few days.

If you are reasonably active, you will find that before long, walking upstairs, doing housework, gardening and lawn mowing become easier and you should have less or no huffing and puffing. On the other hand, if you don't attend to this, you can severely slow down your progress.

Remember: You *do* need more air when you are moving. Breathing should increase naturally, appropriate to the level of exertion, and the breaths should still be through your nose. Let it happen naturally – neither restrict the amount of air you take in through your nose nor exaggerate it by deliberately trying to take in more air. As always, 'comfortable' is the operative word.

The golden rule of nose breathing: *Go only as fast as your nose will comfortably allow.*

Try Practice Set C below, taking into account your usual exercise capacity.

PRACTICE SET C: NOSE BREATHING DURING MOVEMENT

1. Start with a three-minute leisurely walk on flat ground.
2. Pace yourself so that you can breathe comfortably in and out your nose. Comfortably – not torturingly.)
3. If you feel breathless, or that you must open your mouth, slow down or stop and rest until nose breathing is comfortable again. Then start walking again at a slower pace.
4. Try to nose breathe during all your walking and usual physical activities: climbing stairs, bending, lifting, and getting in and out of the car.
5. Increase your walking speed, distance and the incline as your breathing improves.

I accompany elderly clients (including some using portable oxygen cylinders) to their cars after their first appointments, and they're amazed by how much easier they can walk when they consciously nose breathe. We may take slightly longer to get to the car, but once there they do not need to recover from breathlessness.

When nose breathing during walking is second nature, introduce it into other forms of exercise you do, such as cycling or using the treadmill or rowing machine at the gym. Again, choose a pace that is comfortable for nose breathing. You may need to go slower for the first few days. In the long run, your breathing becomes more efficient and you will soon get back to your old speed. Because you are oxygenating better, you may well end up going faster than before. Breathing well during exercise, sport and more strenuous physical activity is covered more fully in Chapter 20.

Amanda, 12, was referred for breathing retraining by her dentist. Her chronic mouth breathing had led to a narrow upper palate and crowded teeth. She snored like a trooper, but had no nasal blockage. She just felt she could not get enough air through her nose to be comfortable. Through breathing retraining, Amanda quickly adjusted to needing less air. By day three, she was comfortably nose breathing all day and night. On day five, she easily jogged 400 metres and then sprinted 200 metres with her mouth closed.

NOSE BREATHING DURING TRANSFERS

People commonly revert to mouth breathing when changing position or situation – during 'transfers' – like getting up from a chair, going from a warm house into cold air, getting in and out of the car, bending down to put their socks on. Doing a short breath hold while you transfer can be extremely useful in preventing mouth breathing and breathlessness.

STRATEGIES FOR NOSE BREATHING DURING SLEEP

Anything that increases your breathing rate in the day or evening may affect the tendency to mouth breathe and over-breathe during sleep. This worsens insomnia, snoring and restless sleep. If you vent off carbon dioxide in excessive quantities while you sleep, you will lose some of the beneficial effects of minding your breathing during the day. Here are some suggestions to prevent over-breathing and to facilitate nose breathing during sleep.

Nose breathe all day

The more you nose breathe during the day, the better you'll adapt to a smaller tidal volume while asleep and the more likely you'll be able to continue nose breathing.

Practise nose breathing before bed

Practise nose breathing Practice Set A or B for two five-minute periods, with a one-minute rest in between them, during the half-hour before bed.

Sleep on your side

The position of heaviest breathing during sleep is flat on your back with your mouth open and your arms up over your head. Many people find their breathing is most gentle when lying on the left side.

Sleep with your upper body elevated

The flatter you lie, generally the heavier you breathe, the more effort it takes, and the more likely you are to breathe through your mouth.

Elevating the head end of the bed about 10–15 cm in the early stages of breathing retraining, or when you have a cold, can make nose breathing easier (see Figure 13.2). This can be done by placing folded blankets between the mattress and bed base, packing pillows

DON'T PANIC!

Long-term mouth breathers and people who experience claustro-phobia, anxiety or panic attacks may have feelings of panic when they initially attempt nose breathing, even when there is no nasal blockage or congestion. For some, just sitting with their mouth closed for a couple of seconds can make them feel panicky. They are so conditioned to breathing a large volume of air, that when they breathe less with their mouth shut, they feel they are suffocating.

It is important then to make changes gradually to allow the body time to adjust. I have found the best way to begin is how I introduced this in Chapter 5, using the Cloud Exercise. This is a very gentle yet profound way of achieving continuous nose breathing.

For some clients a change first in food choices (Chapter 9) or posture (Chapter 14) is helpful. If none of these suggestions help, consult your doctor who may be able to find another cause for an elevated drive to breathe.

PANIC ATTACK RELIEF

Chapter 22 has two versions of the 3 x 3 exercise that are useful to quickly reduce anxiety or quell a panic attack.

in a wedge shape or using specially designed foam wedges to elevate your upper body. Be careful when using extra pillows not to bend your neck in such a way as to contribute to snoring or neck pain. A flat mattress with just one pillow is usually quite sufficient for people who breathe correctly.

Note: Although side-sleeping is the preferred position for better breathing, some spinal, musculoskeletal and other medical conditions may make this sleeping position inadvisable. Please consult your doctor or other healthcare provider if you are unsure.

FIGURE 13.2: ELEVATED SIDE-SLEEPING

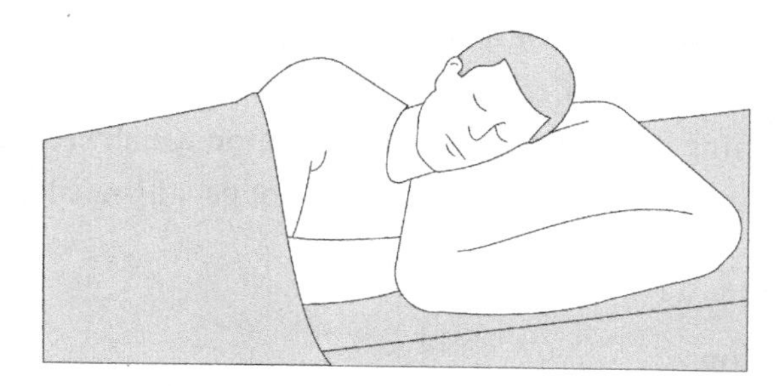

Things to avoid

The Action Steps on page 107 have suggestions for some things to avoid in the evening – all of which can make you 'breathe up' and more likely to mouth breathe during sleep.

Over-sleeping. For most adults, seven to eight hours of quality sleep a night is enough. It is best to sleep only when you are tired, and to get up as soon as you wake in the morning. As your breathing improves, you may find you wake earlier. If you go back to sleep again, you are more likely to wake later with signs of over-breathing.

Eve noticed that she woke at 5.30 am feeling refreshed and with a clear nose, but when she decided to get some extra sleep and woke again at 7 am, she felt tired and blocked up.

EXTRA STRATEGIES FOR UNBLOCKING 'RESISTANT' NOSES

Diet change

Persistent nasal congestion often responds to a change in diet, particularly a reduction in milk (for some) and high-sugar/high-starch foods (see Chapter 9).

Saline nasal sprays

The mucus membranes lining the nose need to be kept moist to effectively clear the inhaled air of dust, germs and pollens. This protective role is compromised when the air is too dry, like in an aircraft, or when you are dehydrated through over-breathing. If you suffer from long-term nasal congestion, you may benefit from using a saline (salt and water) nasal spray. These are available from pharmacies.

Salt solutions are valued for their anti-septic, anti-inflammatory and anti-allergen properties. The effect is not dissimilar to the great nose-clearing effect of swimming in the ocean. Nasal congestion usually responds quickly to breathing retraining and nasal sprays are not usually needed on an ongoing basis.

Nasal medications

Various prescription and over-the-counter medications treat nasal problems. Speak to your doctor or pharmacist about the appropriate type for you and correct usage. Overuse of medicated decongestants can cause rebound congestion.

Surgery

Some nasal problems do require surgery. For example, there may be an anatomical obstruction following trauma that prevents adequate airflow through the nose.

HOW LONG BEFORE I CAN NOSE BREATHE?

The time it should take to achieve 100 per cent nose breathing will vary according to many factors, including the nature, severity and duration of the problem, your level of awareness, your commitment to practising, and which medical treatments you have had or currently use. Even your sleeping position, posture and diet are factors.

In my experience, most people can break a mouth breathing habit within two to five days, providing any nasal obstruction is not primarily structural, and it rarely is. I often see people breathing freely through their nose halfway through their first breathing session, when they are on the waiting list for an ear, nose and throat specialist! Many clients have reported that polyps and adenoids have reduced in size following breathing retraining, and this has been verified by scans and physical examinations.

FAILURE TO ACHIEVE CONTINUOUS NOSE BREATHING

The most common reasons for this include:

- lack of awareness
- activities/walking/exercising with mouth open
- sleeping with mouth open
- high-sugar/high-starch diet
- continued nasal inflammation due to the above
- poor posture
- chronic allergy or infection in nose, sinuses, mouth, teeth or throat needing medical or dental treatment.

The less common reasons include:

- anatomical obstruction needing surgery
- severe COPD.

GOOD BREATHING IS MORE THAN NOSE BREATHING

Breathing through your nose does not necessarily mean that your breathing is perfect. The breaths can still be too big and too often. While it is a big step in the right direction for a mouth breather, you can still be over-breathing. The other healthy habits deal with this.

COPING WITH A COLD

Improving your breathing can make a big difference in preventing and relieving head colds. Firstly, becoming a gentle nose breather gives protection against airborne infective particles. If you do develop a cold, an increase in breathing rate will be part of the inflammatory process. Anything you can do to calm and control your breathing will help reduce symptoms and overcome the acute illness faster.

The 3 x 3 exercise, the sequence of short breath holds described on page 98, can be very helpful. It is used to gently raise carbon dioxide, which can:

- prevent mast cells in the airway releasing histamine

- reduce nasal congestion and inflammation
- slow and calm breathing.

You may find five minutes' practice helpful in relieving congestion. Try it several times during the day and just before bed. Other strategies include side-sleeping and elevating the head end of the bed. Also avoid foods and drinks that increase your breathing rate – they will elevate your nasal congestion and mucus production. For most people, the worst culprits are strong tea, coffee, milk, and high-starch/high-sugar foods.

Take care with nose blowing – only blow if necessary, and then as gently as you can. Follow nose blowing with a short breath hold. You may find use of a saline nasal spray useful.

People who have successfully normalised their breathing usually find that colds become less frequent and shorter.

Jackie had asthma and got frequent colds that would go to her chest every time. Anything going around the office, you could be sure that Jackie would get it first, come down with it hardest, and be off work for longer than anyone else. At a six-month follow-up Jackie very excitedly told me that she had just gone through a whole winter without having a day off work. The first cold she caught had just stayed in her nose and there was no sign of asthma. The next cold that struck her office wiped out everyone else but left her untouched.

Even with a cold, you should still breathe as much as possible through your nose. If it is too congested and you have to resort to mouth breathing for a time, be mindful to breathe as gently through your mouth as you can. *Volume control* of your mouth breathing is an important element in reducing symptoms including nasal congestion.

Rose had been working hard in the garden and was so looking forward to the massage she had booked. However, she had a heavy cold and when she lay face down on the massage table, her nose and sinuses immediately felt full and blocked. There was no way she could nose breathe, which was her normal habit since breathing retraining. She remembered what I had taught her, and breathed as gently through her mouth as was comfortable – enough air, but not excessive. When she stood up at the end of the massage, to her pleasant surprise, her nose was completely clear and comfortable to breathe through.

ACTION STEPS FOR NOSE BREATHING (DAYTIME)

- Awareness – spot-check yourself for mouth breathing.
- Try to breathe only through your nose.
- Aim to increase the percentage of time you nose breathe each day.
- Let your ability to comfortably nose breathe dictate the pace of walking. 
- Go slow now to be faster later.
- If you have to mouth breathe, do so as gently as you can.
- Avoid unbalanced high-sugar/high-starch meals; avoid milk (for some).
- Practise Set A or B once every waking hour until continuous nose breathing is easy.

ACTION STEPS FOR NOSE BREATHING (NIGHT-TIME)

- Nose breathe during the day.
- Sleep with your upper body slightly elevated.
- Avoid sleeping on your back.
- Sleep with your mouth closed.
- Avoid exercising within three hours of bedtime.
- Allow two to three hours after eating before bed.
- Avoid large meals of an evening; avoid high-starch/high-sugar meals.
- Avoid alcohol at night.
- Avoid over-heating and over-sleeping.
- Practise Set A or B for two five-minute periods before bed.
- Consider a saline nasal spray in the initial stages.

ACTION STEPS FOR DEALING WITH A COLD

In addition to the suggestions above:

- Try five minutes' practice of the 3 x 3 exercise for relief of nasal congestion.
- If you have to mouth breathe as your nose is blocked, make it as gentle as you can.
- Rest more but don't sleep more than usual.
- If possible, recline rather than lie down to rest during the day.

When to move on

You can move on to Healthy Habit Three – Upright posture – after two days of nose breathing practice, which you began in Chapter 5. If you are not yet completely nose breathing, move on anyway, as a more upright posture makes nose breathing easier. Just keep up the strategies and practice as above until nose breathing – at rest, while sleeping and during activity – become second nature. The dietary suggestions in Chapter 9 may also be helpful.

Even if you must continue to mouth breathe because your health condition will not allow comfortable nose breathing, many benefits come by making improvements in the other breathing habits. Even mouth breathing in a gentler and more controlled manner than you are used to is a terrific step forward.

CHAPTER 14

Healthy habit three: Upright posture

I hope I haven't caught you sitting with your shoulders slouched while glued to this book, your abdomen folded over, your head down, your chin forward – and breathing using your upper chest! When looking at ways to bring breathing back to normal, posture is very important.

The diaphragm is the main muscle of breathing. With a slumped posture, its action is compromised. When you are folded over, you are compressing the lower chest and the abdomen. Breathing rate and nervous tension increase, as does the likelihood of upper-chest breathing, mouth breathing and over-breathing. Once the chest muscles are too involved, breathing volume goes up by 50–80 per cent.

On the other hand, good posture optimises your breathing. Combined with nose breathing, it automatically facilitates diaphragmatic breathing.

ATTITUDES AND EMOTIONS AFFECT POSTURE

Your attitudes and emotional state can be reflected in your posture, in how you carry yourself. Depression has been linked with a stooped posture. It is hard to feel 'up' when you are 'dumped' down – slumped in a 'C' shape, instead of the healthy 'S' shaped spine. I have observed many anxious teenagers and adults sitting folded in such a way that they appear to be trying to hide. Adjusting your posture adjusts your breathing directly and your emotions indirectly.

Another area affected by poor posture is the throat and voice. A slumped posture and a tense posture can create narrowing in the throat, and tension and dysfunction in the vocal cords.

MYTHS ABOUT POSTURE

Unfortunately, there are several myths about good posture – so please don't skip this section thinking you already know all about it! Good posture is not about straightness and stiffness. Good posture is not about effort.

HOW TO ACHIEVE A GOOD POSTURE

The coathanger posture – relaxed, lengthened upright posture

The *coathanger posture* is a simple and effective way to develop better posture and to 'unfold' and 'open up' the typical slumped posture. It uses the notions of *letting go* and *allowing* – you relax and let the correct positions and movements simply happen. This is more about *undoing* than consciously doing an action; the latter often creates tension and effort. Some of these ideas are also part of the Alexander Technique, a system that helps to achieve good posture and free body movement with minimum effort and strain.

FIGURE 14.1: SITTING IN THE COATHANGER POSTURE

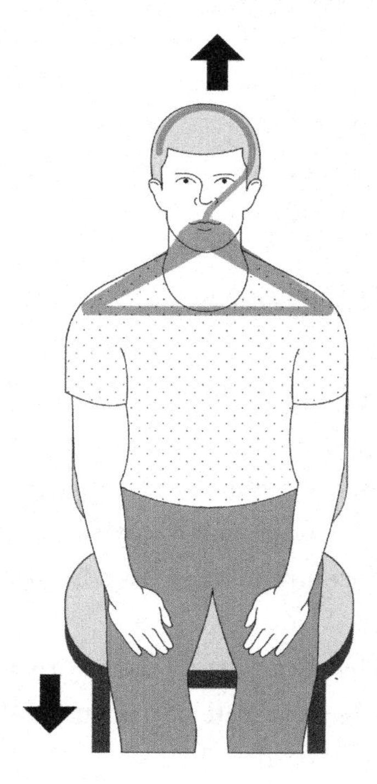

Instructions for sitting

See Figure 14.1. Ideally, choose a firm chair of a height that allows your thighs to be parallel to the ground (and slightly apart), your knees bent at a right angle and your feet flat on the floor. Your hands rest in your lap.

THE SLUMP TEST

After a minute of sitting relaxed with an upright posture, feel where your breathing movement is. Then collapse your posture and sit slumped. Now notice the movement again. Breathing usually goes to the upper chest. Now please sit upright and stay there!

Now imagine having a coathanger inside you – the hook part inside your head and the framework within your shoulder area. Imagine that your coathanger is hung on a railing that's at the perfect height for you. Imagine your body is supported by and softly draping from the internal coathanger. Just relax, unclench and soften your muscles.

Continue to 'let go' and allow yourself to lengthen in two directions: up through the crown of your head and coathanger; down through your sit bones (the bony knobs in your buttocks) into the chair. Allow your weight to drop down. It feels like you are letting your bones take your weight, and your muscles can fully relax, without tension. When you get the relaxation and 'letting go' right, you feel you're getting taller/longer, with more space between your vertebrae. The effect you want is *relaxed, lengthened sitting.*

Also let go of tension in your shoulders and have a soft, relaxed stomach. Your face muscles, jaw and throat also need to be relaxed. Say to yourself, 'Long face, soft jaw, soft throat'. Have your lips touching but your teeth apart.

The idea of the coathanger allows a sense of relaxing the body while at the same time not collapsing and losing height. This feels very different from the tension created by the usual 'sit up straight' command.

How does it feel? Most people feel relaxed; their breathing movement reduces, and breaths are slow and quiet, dropping automatically from the upper chest to the lower ribcage/diaphragm area. This posture also helps you settle your breathing quickly when distressed.

I have put these instructions into the list below. I have also produced the *Breathing Exercise Instruction Audio* (CD or MP3) which goes through the instructions described here and in chapters 16 and 18. Each of the three 10-minute tracks takes you step by step through a full practice session.

Many have found this very helpful (See Learning Resources: Audio aids to learning, page 201.)

PRACTICE SET: RELAXED, LENGTHENED SITTING

How to take up the coathanger posture:

1. Feet flat on the floor; thighs parallel to the ground.
2. Hands relaxed in your lap.
3. Imagine your coathanger in position.
4. Let go of the long muscles down either side of your spine.
5. Allow your neck to soften and lengthen.
6. Allow your body to soften and lengthen – up through your head, down through your sit bones.
7. Relax your shoulders; allow them to soften, widen and drop.
8. Soften your stomach muscles.
9. Relax your jaw; have your lips together, your teeth apart.
10. Have a long face and a soft jaw.
11. Relax your throat, relax your tongue, loosen your throat.
12. Sit in this position and breathe as gently as you can, through your nose, for 5–10 minutes.

PRACTICE TIMES

Until good posture is second nature, aim to check your posture every hour, on the hour. Practise three times a day, 5–10 minutes each time. You can combine this with your nose breathing practice. The best times to practise are before getting dressed in the morning, before you go to bed and whenever you have some spare time in your day – such as on the train, while in a waiting room or while on hold on the phone.

Instructions for standing and walking

When you have a relaxed diaphragm and a lengthened spine during standing and all activities, from daily chores, to walking, to running a marathon, healthy breathing becomes easier. The coathanger posture – lengthening upwards through your head and downwards through your tailbone and your feet – can be used equally well with all these activities.

You should progressively work towards the coathanger posture all the time. When you first get out of bed in the morning, imagine putting your coathanger in, looping it over that imaginary railing and allowing your body to drape softly, comfortably and at full length from it. Throughout the day, give yourself cues by asking, 'Am I on my coathanger?' Check your posture when in the car. You may need to adjust the seat to reinforce a better posture.

Undoing the damage

People who have had poor posture for years have probably compensated for it and have weak or tight muscles and stiff joints as a result. When you first improve your posture while sitting, it can be tiring and feel unnatural. You may benefit by using pillows to help prop and support you. While some of us may be able to achieve good posture through awareness and attention, it is desirable for those with conditions like scoliosis to have professional help to achieve the best posture they are capable of. I highly recommend the Alexander Technique. Massage, muscle-release therapies and heat packs may also help release tight tissues.

Joanne's psychologist referred her for breathing training, as her anxiety and panic attacks were becoming more disabling and cognitive techniques were not helping them. She also slept poorly and was extremely tired. She snored, had sleep apnoea and restless legs and was waking three to five times every night. Joanne ticked off 48 different signs and symptoms of dysfunctional breathing on the checklist, scoring most of them as severe. I observed her as she went through the checklist: she breathed 12 times a minute with her upper chest, two of which were very large breaths; her spine was in a 'C' shape and she was collapsed over her diaphragm area. I introduced the concept of the coathanger and asked her to try to change her posture gradually over the next few days. That was my only instruction. Joanne experienced a huge shift in the way her body was functioning. Eighteen of her symptoms went away, and another 24 were significantly reduced. There was a dramatic improvement in sleep and energy. She had no panic attacks. Once the edge had been taken off her condition, she joined a breathing course.

THE BENEFITS

The benefits of improving your posture can be extraordinary and far-reaching. I have seen the unfolding of a poor posture reduce or eliminate many symptoms of chronic over-breathing within 24 hours. Most stunning to observe is the lifting of mood and easing of anxiety.

In addition to the benefits to your breathing and your mood, the relaxed upright lengthened posture allows your musculoskeletal system to function most efficiently and fluidly. This will lead to less wear and tear on your joints, less muscle imbalance and less likelihood of chronic pain syndromes. Other benefits are improved sleep, digestion and aesthetics: you'll look better, look taller and your stomach will appear flatter. On the other hand, if you continue to maintain a slumped posture, your ability to achieve normal breathing, good health and a sense of relaxation and calm is severely disadvantaged.

What a difference breathing training and adjusting his office chair and posture made for Mike! Immediately he stopped sighing and holding his breath, and he felt less tense. He no longer had to pump himself full of coffee after lunch to prevent the 3 pm sleepies at his desk.

ACTION STEPS FOR UPRIGHT POSTURE

- Sit, stand and walk with a relaxed, lengthened coathanger posture.
- Check your posture and breathing once an hour.
- Practise *relaxed lengthened sitting* for 5–10 minutes, three times a day, until good posture is automatic.

When to move on

Move on to Healthy Habit Four – Regular breathing – when you have practised at least one day of the relaxed upright posture.

CHAPTER 15

Healthy habit four: Regular breathing

Irregular breathing is common in people with anxiety disorders. Your breathing rhythm is interrupted by episodes of fast or heavier breathing, sniffing, throat clearing, coughing, sighing, yawning, or breath holding. Wide variations in breath size, speed and rhythm are accompanied by wide swings in carbon dioxide. This destabilises your breathing control and blood chemistry. Irregular breathing during the day also sets you up for erratic breathing during sleep.

Breathing retraining by day aims to bring back control, smoothness and regularity to your breathing and stabilise your blood chemistry. It helps you to have smoother, gentler, quieter breathing at night.

Coughing

There are several potential causes of coughing and it is important to have the cause identified and appropriately treated. An irritable, dry, tickly cough can occur without a medically known cause, but it is certainly worsened by mouth breathing.

Coughing, because it is so forceful, can be quite abusive to your airway, with each cough further dehydrating and irritating the airway and provoking the next cough. For those with asthma, coughing may provoke bronchospasm. Coughing can also constrict blood vessels, raise your blood pressure and be a strain on your heart. It can be exhausting.

Breathing retraining aims to reduce mouth breathing, over-breathing, and dry, tickly coughing and thereby protect your airways from irritation and excessive physical forces.

STRATEGIES FOR SMOOTH, REGULAR BREATHING

Reducing dry, tickly coughing, throat clearing, yawning, sighing

SHORT BREATH HOLD

Short breath holds were first introduced in Chapter 13. They can be a valuable tool for stopping large, forceful breaths such as dry, tickly coughing, throat clearing, yawning, and sighing. This *prevents* dumping out of carbon dioxide. The short breath hold can also be used after a cough, sigh or yawn to make up for, or *compensate for*, some of the carbon dioxide lost through these excessively big breaths.

The pause in breathing should not be so long that you alter your breathing pattern afterwards. After the short pause, try to coax your breathing back into a smooth wave pattern to prevent further yawning, sighing, coughing, and throat clearing. See Figure 15.1.

PROCEDURE FOR PREVENTION – STOP THE LEAK OF CARBON DIOXIDE

When you feel you are about to cough, yawn, sigh, or clear your throat, try to stop it by:

- closing your mouth
- pausing your breath for a count of three (two to three seconds)
- breathing in and out through your nose, as slowly, gently and smoothly as you can, controlling the rhythm and breath size
- relaxing your breathing and stomach muscles.

Repeat the process if the urge comes again.

PROCEDURE FOR COMPENSATION – MAKING UP THE LOST CARBON DIOXIDE

Use a short breath hold straight after a cough, yawn or sigh if you were unable to stop it (see lower section of Figure 15.1). This way, you compensate for the loss of carbon dioxide by building the level up again. Also, if you cannot block a cough, put your hand over your mouth to prevent yourself from taking a big breath through it.

Remember: Do not pause your breath for so long that it causes the next breath to be excessively large, or you gasp or cough as a result. Breathing retraining is about promoting controlled, silent, gentle breaths. It is about avoiding any negative effects on your breathing.

If you have had a chronic irritable cough, this exercise may need to be used quite frequently to overcome the urge to cough. However, as your breathing improves and the airway becomes less irritated, the cough should settle.

FIGURE 15.1: SHORT BREATH HOLDS FOR COUGH, YAWN AND SIGH

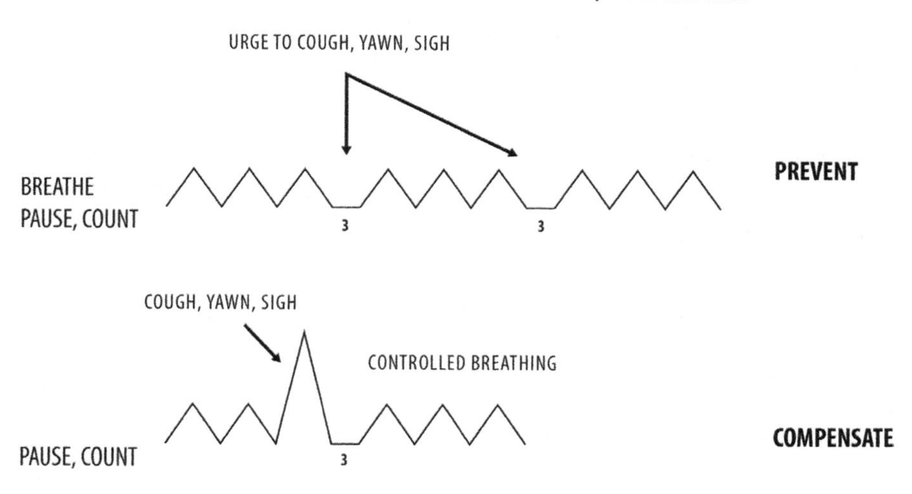

SWALLOW, SIP WATER

A swallow in place of the short breath hold or during it can help you resist a sigh, yawn or cough. Sipping warm water may also help inhibit coughing fits.

> *Madeline, a museum guide, used to cough constantly throughout her tours. All the talking she did made it worse. Her cough stopped as soon as she started the breathing course. She no longer got exhausted from talking all day, did not have to clear mucus from her throat and did not get dehydrated like she used to.*

Moist coughs

Do not suppress your cough when there is mucus in your airway that needs to come up. However, try to cough in a more controlled way. This is particularly important for those with asthma. When mucus needs to be shifted, try to remove it with the minimum amount of coughing that it takes to do so. Follow a bout of coughing with nose breathing – as gentle as possible – and some short breath holds.

When you have to cough, put your hand over your mouth to prevent gulping in so much air, or even try to inhale through your nose, and cough with your mouth closed. This will lessen the irritation on your throat.

If your cough doesn't improve with these suggestions, please consult your doctor.

Nicholas was referred to me by a neurologist. For eight years he had been having several coughing fits every week, which caused him to black out. That was bad enough, but sometimes he would also convulse. Testing had confirmed that it was not epilepsy. But what was it? For some people, repetitive coughing can bring on an asthma attack. For Nicholas, it was most likely that the huge loss of carbon dioxide during his coughing fits was causing a narrowing of blood vessels to his brain. He didn't have a coughing fit in front of me at the clinic, but the signs of a chronic over-breathing pattern were definitely there. After just one session of breathing training there were no further episodes.

Sneezing and nose blowing

Because sneezing is involuntary and explosive, it is harder to control than yawning and sighing. It is also not advisable to inhibit a sneeze after the urge and pressure has built up. Sneezes can exit at over 100 km/hour.

Instead, pause your breath for two to three seconds immediately *after* the first sneeze to try to prevent a series of sneezes. If mucus has accumulated, try to get by with just wiping the end of your nose or with a gentle, small-volume nose blow. Everything connected with breathing should be gentle, including nose blowing. Big honking nose blows will stimulate further mucus production.

PROCEDURE FOR SNEEZING AND NOSE BLOWING

1. Pause your breath for a count of three immediately after the first sneeze.

2. Breathe in and out through your nose, as slowly, gently and smoothly as you can, controlling the rhythm and breath size.
3. Try to get by with just wiping your nose or only gentle, small-volume nose blowing.
4. Avoid honking nose blows.

YAWNING

No-one fully understands why we yawn. Whatever the reason, an odd yawn in the evening, when we are bored or as a copycat behaviour is quite natural. However, repetitive yawning is a marker of dysfunctional breathing and can provoke and perpetuate symptoms. So block it with a short breath hold!

INCREASED YAWNING – THE BATTLE OF THE RESPIRATORY CENTRE

Some people notice an increase in their desire to yawn when they first change their breathing. If you've had chronically low carbon dioxide, which you were maintaining through intermittent sighing, yawning or mouth breathing, it will take some time for your body to acclimatise to the changes you are making.

Your body may at first try to get you over-breathing again, dumping out carbon dioxide in the form of more yawning. It may take a couple of days for the increased desire to yawn to go away. In the meantime, be aware, and do your best to suppress yawns using a short breath hold or 'swallowing' them.

ACTION STEPS FOR REGULAR BREATHING

- Try to breathe gently and smoothly through your nose at all times.
- Allow no jerkiness or irregularities to disturb the steady flow of your breathing.
- Use a short breath hold and/or a swallow to prevent or compensate for a yawn, sigh, dry cough, sneeze, or erratic/ forceful breaths.
- Afterwards, control your breathing rhythm and breath size.
- If you must blow your nose, do so gently.
- If you must cough, do it gently and try to keep your mouth closed, or put your hand over your mouth.
- If you need to breathe through your mouth, make it as smooth and gentle as you possibly can.
- Be diligent while your respiratory centre adapts.

When to move on

For the next 24–48 hours, give some special focus to your breathing rhythm. Become familiar with it and the situations that disturb your rhythm. While you are spending this time gently coaxing your breathing into a steady rhythm in the way just described, continue to pay attention to nose breathing and the relaxed upright posture. They all work together. Then move on to Healthy Habit Five – Diaphragm breathing.

CHAPTER 16

Healthy habit five: Diaphragm breathing

Diaphragm breathing is the most efficient and restful way to breathe. Many people with anxiety are upper-chest breathers. Those who do breathe mainly with their diaphragm often do so incorrectly. Please read on here even if you have previously learnt 'diaphragm breathing'. *Correct* diaphragm breathing is often very different from what people think. For breathing to become easy, natural and normal, many people have to unlearn what they have previously practised.

A MUCH MISUNDERSTOOD MUSCLE

The diaphragm is a thin but powerful dome-shaped muscle situated under your lungs, separating your chest cavity (containing lungs and heart) from your abdominal cavity (containing stomach, liver, intestines and other organs). It is the primary breathing muscle, and its action moves air in and out of the lungs.

In healthy breathers, when the diaphragm contracts, flattens and descends during the in-breath, the contents of the upper abdominal area bulge out a *little* in the solar plexus region. The diaphragm normally moves in coordination with the lower ribs, so at the same time there is a *small* outward movement of the lower ribs at the sides and the back. In other words, you get *slightly* bigger all the way around your body at the upper-waist level – it moves out naturally, passively, you don't 'do' it.

Exhalation is even more passive; it is an 'elastic' recoil of the chest wall, lungs and diaphragm. The diaphragm relaxes, it forms a dome shape again, and the lower ribs and upper abdominal area drop back in a little. Air passes from the lungs back through the upper airways into the atmosphere. The upper chest and lower abdomen are almost still when a healthy breather inhales and exhales.

FIGURE 16.1: THE DIAPHRAGM

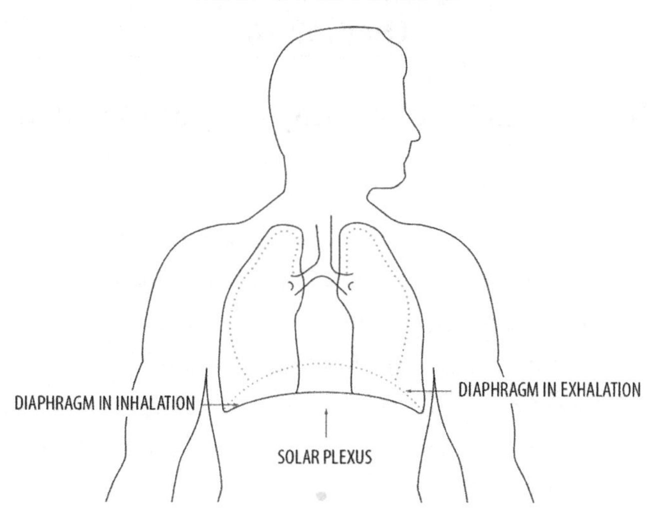

Did you notice the words *slightly*, *small*, *little*, *still*, and *passive* in the above description of what correct diaphragm breathing looks like? As well as being inaudible, healthy breathing is barely visible.

Contrast this with the commonly held belief that the bigger your breath and the larger the outward movement of your lower chest and abdomen, the better your breathing is. I'm sure you've also heard these words of encouragement before: big, deep, expand, fill, push, empty, squeeze, suck in, tighten.

Before we move on to learning how to correctly breathe using the diaphragm, let me run through the most common faults I see. Rest assured that achieving correct diaphragm breathing is usually quite easy. Once you identify and undo your bad habits, you can just let go and relax into the correct way of breathing.

Fault one: Upper-chest breathing

This is where the upper chest moves first or moves more than the diaphragm area. Using your chest and shoulder muscles to breathe 20,000 times a day can be exhausting and leave you with neck and shoulder pain. Even if you don't chest breathe all the time, in times of stress your breathing can fly back up there. Squint your eyes now – what do you notice when you breathe in? Now relax your eyes and take another breath. Feel the difference?

Even mild tension like squinting can send your breathing to your upper chest! Your breathing could be compromised during the day simply by working at your computer in poor light.

Fault two: Rigid abdominal muscles

Consciously or unconsciously tensing the abdominal muscles and 'over effort' to maintain a flat stomach interferes with the movement of the diaphragm and therefore your breathing. I have seen athletes with super-tight abs and flat stomachs suffer performance anxiety, panic attacks, shortness of breath, and poor endurance because of their upper-chest breathing pattern.

I've also found disordered breathing, anxiety states and digestive issues in people who have been working hard at improving 'core stability' but in effect have been holding in their stomachs all the time and driving their breathing into their upper chest.

Sarah was a very fit but rather 'wired' 21-year-old when she came to see me. Not only was she anxious, but she slept poorly and was exhausted all the time. She would get intensely anxious and spaced-out when working with her fitness trainer or doing Pilates classes. It took Sarah a few days of breathing retraining to undo the abdominal tension she had worked so hard at, but she is now enjoying her fitness sessions as well as refreshing sleep.

Fault three: Belly puffing

This is where you actively use your abdominal muscles to push your belly area out as you breathe in. It is common to see people practising 'belly puffing' and erroneously calling it diaphragmatic breathing. It is *not* natural and it is *not* helpful.

By pushing your abdomen out with every breath, you can end up arching your lower back and creating strain and even pain in the process. It's even worse if you're trying to do that against those tight abs you've been working on. And you're not increasing your lung capacity. The bottom of your lungs is about seven cm below your nipple line!

Fault four: Forced exhalation

You may have learnt the practice of fully, even forcefully exhaling in fitness training or a Pilates, yoga or singing class, but it is not physiologically normal to do so. Nor is it good for you. A series of forced exhalations, sometimes even just one, can blow off sufficient carbon dioxide to constrict arteries to the brain, resulting in dizziness or panic, or constrict your bronchial tubes leading to breathlessness or asthma.

At the end of a normal relaxed exhalation, we are meant to have over a litre of air remaining in our lungs. This is called the 'expiratory reserve volume'. See Figure 16.2. During strenuous activity, larger in-breaths and out-breaths are normal. Some or all of this reserve capacity will be used, naturally and automatically, and still not forcefully.

SPECIAL EFFECTS BREATHING

Large-volume diaphragm breathing exercises may have a place if you have an area of collapse or consolidation in your lungs. This may occur with pneumonia, or after an anaesthetic. But then you are practising those exercises for a 'special effect' or therapeutic purpose – you are not practising *normal* or *correct* breathing. When you finish doing 'deep-breathing' exercises you need to be aware of the potential consequences (for example, dizziness, fatigue and shortness of breath) of consciously or unconsciously continuing to breathe too much air per breath. You need to know to return to normal, gentle, nose-diaphragm breathing as soon as possible after deep breathing (and coughing).

Fault five: Misunderstanding diaphragm breathing

I use the term *diaphragm breathing* to mean breathing *correctly* with the diaphragm. This means you draw in your air mainly through diaphragm movement, but also that the size of the breath, and therefore the size of diaphragm movement, is appropriate for the situation, be it rest, sleep or activity.

However, people often incorrectly associate the term diaphragm breathing with a deliberate increase in breath size and filling more of your lungs. At rest, the physiologically correct breath size or tidal volume is around 500 ml. Our lungs have the capacity to take in considerably more – up to 3,000 ml extra – and our

diaphragm can move through a greater range to allow us to draw it in. So, compared to breathing your full lung capacity, normal resting breathing is *small-volume diaphragm breathing.* See 'tidal volume' in Figure 16.2.

A deep – big, full-capacity – breath is not appropriate unless you are doing vigorous physical exercise. Then it is natural to inhale some of your 'inspiratory reserve capacity' and dip into your expiratory reserve volume (see Figure 16.2), but it's not appropriate in a meditation or Pilates class or while you hold a yoga pose.

FIGURE 16.2: LUNG VOLUMES

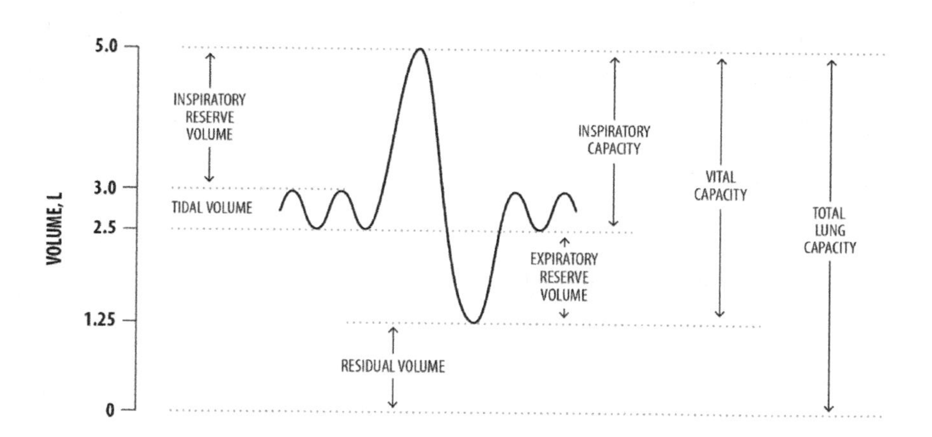

Sometimes people are told to 'direct' the air to between the navel and the pubic bone. That's a long way from where the lungs and diaphragm are!

So, in common usage, the terms *deep breathing* and *abdominal breathing* refer to taking large in-breaths with diaphragm action and possibly some belly puffing as well, and then fully exhaling, emptying the lungs of as much air as possible. In common practice then, deep or abdominal breathing exercises are *large-volume diaphragm breathing.*

HOW TO BREATHE CORRECTLY WITH THE DIAPHRAGM

If by now you have established nose breathing and a relaxed upright posture, your diaphragm will automatically be more involved. Tension in your diaphragm may also have eased – muscle relaxation is yet another wonderful side-effect of addressing over-breathing.

The suggestions below aim to further improve diaphragm breathing. Enjoy the practice. Correct diaphragm breathing has a very relaxing effect on your nervous system and naturally reduces over-breathing.

The 'soft gold band'

As described earlier, the movement of your body as you breathe should occur at the lower end of your ribcage at the sides and back as well as in the solar plexus at the front. It is important to develop a feel for this area – where the movement is when breathing is right.

It can help to imagine you have a 10-cm-wide band of skin all around your body just below the end of your breastbone that is gold in colour: your *soft gold band*. It is like a wide, high, soft-elastic waistband (that is, it has 'give' in it). It expands as you breathe in, and falls back into place as you breathe out.

FIGURE 16.3: BREATHING USING YOUR SOFT GOLD BAND

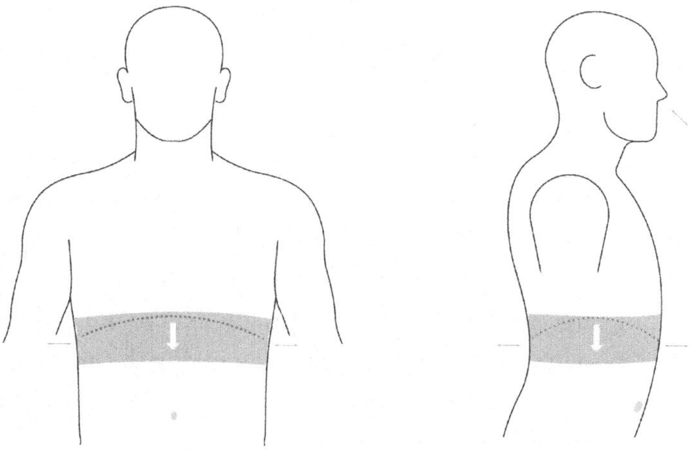

Instructions for diaphragm breathing

Read through the following and practise each suggestion as you go, and then I will put it all together in a list, the Practice Set for diaphragm breathing.

Avoid doing the practice straight after a meal or when wearing a belt or overly tight clothing, which interfere with free diaphragm movement. Also, do not practise this when driving.

Sit in the relaxed coathanger posture, in a chair with an upright padded backrest (or use pillows to support your back). Imagine your soft gold band all around your body. As you breathe in, the gold band area should expand slightly – that is, on the in-breath you (passively) get slightly bigger all the way around at the diaphragm level. On the out-breath the area falls back in. Can you feel this?

Relax your breathing muscles to allow correct breathing to happen. As well as letting go of the trunk, stomach and abdominal muscles you learnt in Chapter 14, think of your dome-shaped diaphragm muscle (under that soft gold band) being soft, relaxed, even 'lazy', 50 per cent made of jelly, or think of it operating on four cylinders instead of eight. Then, as these muscles relax, let your breathing become lighter – simply *let it happen*. Do not try to breathe to a rhythm; do not try to slow your breathing down.

Gently, softly, breathe in, just the right volume of air for you, and direct this air into the soft gold band area – front, sides and back. Place the palm of your hand on your solar plexus. Feel for an outward movement under your hand as your gold band expands. Then, as your out-breath happens, feel the area under your hand fall back in. Simply allow the out-breath to happen passively; then allow the next in-breath to 'arrive' when it's ready. Just allow it to happen passively, like a balloon inflating and deflating of its own accord.

At the completion of breathing in, there should be no holding of the breath, but a turn and flow into the out-breath. Throughout the whole process, think of softening your stomach muscles and *letting go*.

Now, take your hand away and while continuing to breathe 'lazily' into the soft gold band area, notice if you can feel outward movement on each side of your back, just below your shoulder blades, where your back touches the backrest of your chair. When you breathe in, you should feel yourself get slightly bigger there.

If you cannot feel the breath moving your back, try specifically directing the air there. Again, don't exaggerate the breath; just allow it and the movement to happen. Get your controlling self out of the way. Say to yourself,

'I allow my back to be breathed' as you gently and rhythmically breathe through your nose. Allow the breath to be completely effortless; have as much air per breath and as many breaths as you need to stay completely comfortable. Closing your eyes may help.

If you feel short of breath, this may mean you are forcing your breathing to be lighter than it wants to be at this stage. The respiratory centre in your brainstem is being challenged by a higher (probably more normal) carbon dioxide level, and if the challenge is too great, this can then make you want to 'breathe up' again. Remember, have as much air as you need to stay comfortable and in control. Acclimatise at a comfortable pace.

Many people find it easier to develop relaxed diaphragm breathing by directing the air and their attention to the movement in their back rather than the solar plexus. You could imagine the air that comes in through your nose going down one single pipe, which divides into two pipes, which open into each of your lungs in the area below each shoulder blade (see Figure 16.4).

FIGURE 16.4: BREATHING INTO YOUR BACK

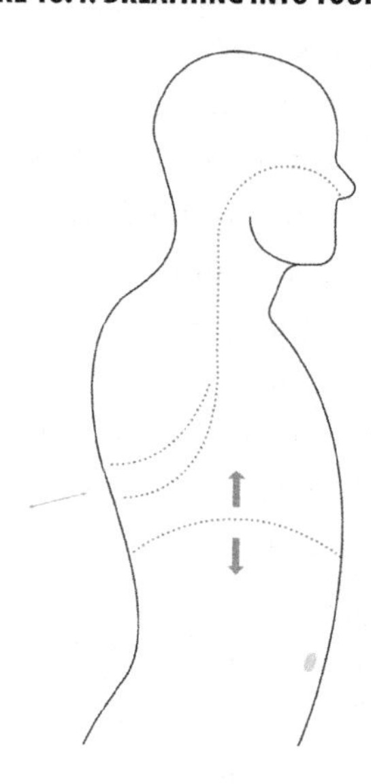

When diaphragm breathing is correctly done, you sense your breathing being lighter, while at the same time the breath is still going down into the soft gold band area – solar plexus, back and side ribs – even if your focus is on the back. When you relax the air out, you know there is still some air left in your lungs.

I recommend that you use your hand on your solar plexus and your back up against a padded backrest *only* in the very beginning. When you are more tuned in, you should be able to maintain relaxed diaphragm breathing without any prompts. In fact, keeping a hand on the solar plexus can encourage active abdominal movement – puffing the belly out – which interferes with correct diaphragm action.

It is also important that you don't try to expand the soft gold band area by breathing in a larger volume of air than you need. Simply allow the breathing to happen in this area. Good breathing is more 'let go and allow it to happen' than 'do it this way'.

What about reducing upper-chest movement? With relaxed diaphragm breathing, upper-chest and shoulder movement almost always gradually and naturally diminishes.

PRACTICE SET: DIAPHRAGM BREATHING

The instructions below put together all the concepts used so far for retraining good breathing. You are practising the first five healthy habits all at once. As before, it may help to listen to these instructions when you are sitting practising. (See Learning Resources: Breathing Exercise Instruction Audio page 201.)

1. Settle into the relaxed, lengthened coathanger posture.
2. Relax your jaw; have your lips together, your teeth apart.
3. Allow your body to soften and lengthen – up through your head, down through your sit bones.
4. Relax your shoulders; soften your stomach.
5. Breathe gently and smoothly through your nose.
6. Become aware of a relaxed (soft, jelly-like, lazy) diaphragm.
7. Allow your breathing to lower into the soft gold band.
8. Relax and allow the gold band to expand on the in-breath.
9. Flow into the out-breath, soften your stomach muscles.
10. Breathe softly, smoothly, into the gold band.

11. Relax, let go on the out-breath.
12. Simply allow the next breath to arrive when it is ready.
13. Allow your back to be gently breathed.
14. Relax, soften your stomach, let go on the out-breath.
15. Breathe as softly and smoothly as you can.

PRACTICE TIMES

Practise relaxed diaphragm breathing two to three times a day, for 10 to 20 minutes total each time.

Ideal times to practise are on waking, just before bed and once or twice more over the course of the day. You could:

- start the day either with a 10–15-minute seated session, or lying in bed on your back with your knees bent
- do 10–20 minutes' practice before bed
- practise while watching TV, on the bus, waiting for a meeting, in coffee breaks, waiting on the phone, or standing in a queue
- lie on your side and practise for a few minutes to help you go off to sleep.

Although you can use this technique anywhere, you might become very relaxed, similar to a meditative state. As with any sort of meditation, you should not undertake this focused diaphragm breathing practice while driving or operating machinery.

Checking your heart rate

Check your heart rate before and one minute after a practice session, while still sitting. If you have done the breathing well, your heart rate should reduce or stay the same. If your heart rate goes up by six beats or more a minute, you are likely not doing it correctly – your body is under stress. Compare your heart rate now to your resting heart rate that you recorded in Table 1.1 on page 6.

DIAPHRAGM BREATHING WHEN WALKING – MUCH EASIER FOR SOME!

Some people find it easier to practise breathing while standing or walking around. If you feel 'antsy' or unsettled sitting down, get up and give it a go.

The principles are the same as for sitting. Remember though, that when you are moving, your body requires more air and produces more carbon dioxide relative to the intensity of the activity, so it is natural to breathe more.

THE BIGGEST MISTAKE

The biggest mistake people make with diaphragm breathing practice is to increase their tidal volume and end up over-breathing. This may happen if you have been conditioned by past training to take full breaths whenever you think or hear the word 'diaphragm'. You *can* undo that conditioning.

I suggest you first practice relaxed nose-diaphragm breathing during a 5–10-minute walk on the flat. Maintain the relaxed coathanger posture. Think of free expansion of your soft gold band area on inhalation, and the sense of allowing your back to be breathed, and having a soft, stomach and 'uninvolved' abs. You will naturally draw in more air per breath to match any increased need for air. Make the out-breath effortless, and allow the next breath to arrive in its own time.

Once you have the concept, you can practise nose-diaphragm breathing during your normal activities. Remember always to walk, cycle, mow, and scrub only at the speed at which nose breathing remains completely comfortable. You will probably breathe more softly and effortlessly than you used to. Even though you may take longer to get places at first, there should be less of the breathlessness, congestion, coughing, and exhaustion that came with poorly controlled breathing. Hopefully within a week or two, nose-diaphragm breathing during all your activities will be your new habit and will need little thought.

We take breathing control during physical exercise and sport further in Chapter 20.

ACTION STEPS FOR DIAPHRAGM BREATHING

- Sit, stand and walk in the relaxed, lengthened coathanger posture.
- Breathe smoothly and gently through your nose and with your diaphragm.
- Allow your back to be *gently* breathed.
- Blend relaxed nose–diaphragm breathing into all your activities.
- Practise two to three times a day, for 10 to 20 minutes,

until nose-diaphragm breathing is second nature.

- Check your posture and breathing once every hour.

Reassess your breathing pattern (Table 1.1 page 6 and symptoms (Table 3.1 pages 24-25) after two days of diaphragm breathing.

When to move on

Spend at least two days focusing on relaxed diaphragm breathing when you are sitting practising, resting and moving around. Move on when nose-diaphragm breathing feels natural. If progress is slow, paying attention to your diet (Chapter 9) and to the way you breathe when you speak (Chapter 19) may help.

Struggling? – Take a 'Three-Day Holiday'!

I use the concept of declaring a 'three-day holiday' when I suspect that people have been going at the changes too hard; being too controlling, overly focused on improving their breathing and more or less forcing their body into a new pattern of diaphragm breathing or nose breathing, faster than it's ready for. The three-day holiday usually works brilliantly. Check it out in Chapter 21.

CHAPTER 17

Healthy habit six: Eight to twelve breaths per minute

This element of healthy breathing doesn't need specific practice because it tends to follow naturally from developing the other good habits. Your breathing automatically slows down as you change from mouth to nose breathing, and as you change from chest to diaphragm breathing.

You do not need to watch a clock and practise doing 8–12 breaths a minute. In fact, I advise against it. Deliberately breathing slower to a count may result in you compensating by breathing too heavily or too deeply. It is better to simply relax into gentle diaphragm breathing and let the timing sort itself out automatically.

How does your respiration rate now compare to normal? And to what it was in the breathing quiz (Table 1.1, page 6)? If it was higher than normal and has decreased, you're on the right track. If it has not, it looks like you need more practice of gentle diaphragm breathing, or you need to work out what is making you 'breathe up'.

Remember: Your respiration rate is affected by the foods you eat, the medications you take, illness, and the stress you are under. The average respiration rate for my clients beginning a breathing retraining program is just over 16 breaths per minute. The average a week later is around 11 breaths a minute.

CHAPTER 18

Healthy habit seven: Silent invisible breathing

Most people who improve their breathing reduce both their breathing rate and breath size. This naturally leads to quieter and less visible breathing.

THE SOUND OF YOUR BREATHING

Good breathing is silent. As you work at eliminating mouth breathing and erratic and forceful breaths, airway irritation lessens. So should your noise level when you're awake and asleep.

Can you hear yourself breathing now?

Can you hear yourself breathing while moving about?

How does that compare to before?

Has anyone commented that you breathe more quietly?

Now add some conscious effort to reducing any remaining noise level during the day. If your breathing is audible when doing light activities, slow down and see if it quietens while still comfortably nose breathing. Do you need to huff and puff getting out of your chair?

'INVISIBLE' BREATHING

Sense how much your torso moves as you breathe. Ideally, with quiet resting breathing, there is virtually no movement seen or felt in the upper chest/collarbone/shoulder area and in the abdominal area below the navel. There is just a small movement of the soft gold band area – solar plexus and lower side and back ribs. Good breathing is almost invisible as well as silent.

At this stage into changing your breathing, if you had a high tidal volume to begin with, it is likely to be considerably less now than when you first picked up this book, but still likely higher than the ideal 500 ml. You are not quite perfect yet. But practice makes perfect and permanent.

The best way to progress is through further relaxation while you practise diaphragm breathing. Your breathing rate and breath size (volume) decrease during relaxation as your need for air (oxygen) is less. You also need less oxygen as your breathing gets more efficient. You use a lot more oxygen with upper-chest breathing. Those muscles are not designed for continuous usage and are very greedy for oxygen.

Practise all exercises with a relaxed, lengthened posture, relaxed diaphragm and shoulders, and let your breathing be comfortable at all times. You should not feel distressed in any way, breathless or short of air.

HIBERNATION

To move closer towards silent and 'invisible' breathing, I use the analogy of hibernation. Hibernation is a natural physiological state in which certain animals pass the winter. It is marked by deep sleep, a reduction in temperature, metabolism, heart rate and breathing rate, and a super degree of muscle relaxation. Try the following routine. This can also be practised while listening to a recording of the instructions. (See Learning Resources: Audio aids to learning, Breathing Exercise Instruction Audio page 201.)

PRACTICE SET: HIBERNATION

1. Sit in a comfortable chair, in the coathanger posture.
2. Allow your shoulders to soften, widen and drop.
3. Breathe smoothly and regularly through your nose.
4. Focus on relaxed, soft gold band diaphragm breathing.
5. Soften your stomach muscles.
6. Allow your back to be gently breathed, then…
7. Pretend you are a bear sinking into hibernation, where all your body processes slow down:
    - Think of your diaphragm relaxing further, moving through less distance.
    - Imagine half its muscle fibres are having time off.
    - Visualise the other half gradually relaxing, peacefully contracting.

- Allow your back to be more and more gently breathed, as you drift further into 'hibernation' – a fuller relaxation of all your breathing muscles – less, but enough, air per breath.
- Visualise the breathing wave pattern gradually getting smaller.
- Allow your breathing to gradually lighten and quieten.
- Allow the inhale to arrive when it's ready.
- Relax, simply let go on the out-breath.
- Breathe 'invisibly'; breathe almost 'as if you are not breathing'.

8. Spend two to five minutes hibernating like this. Have a break for one minute and repeat.
9. If you find this comfortable, try to build up to doing 10 minutes continuously.

PRACTICE TIMES

Make this your way of practising your diaphragm breathing for a total time of 10 minutes, practised three to four times a day. That can be on the bus on the way to work, in quiet times before lunch and dinner and most importantly, for 10 minutes immediately before you go to bed. If you have more time available you can, if you wish, extend the total time of a practice session to 20 minutes.

Let me emphasise again, this technique may induce a state of very significant relaxation, similar to the meditative state, and therefore you should not practise it, or any form of focused relaxed diaphragm breathing, while driving or operating machinery.

VARIATION – 'BACK OF THE NOSE BREATHING'

For some people, focusing their attention on the diaphragm or solar plexus area moving with the gentle breath can actually make them uncomfortable. We can't have that in breathing retraining.

What usually works very well instead, during invisible/hibernation breathing practice, is to put your focus on the most gentle, smallest breath that is *comfortable*, imagining each new breath entering your nostrils and going in only as far as the back of the nose or throat, before turning and relaxing out. Allow it in, relax, let it go out.

When you are comfortable and familiar with the hibernation exercise, you may extend it with the instructions below.

STILLNESS AFTER THE OUT-BREATH – THE NATURAL PAUSE

The natural and spontaneous rest point in the breathing cycle is after the exhale. Your breathing muscles and nervous system rest at this point. As your breathing improves, a short but distinct 'automatic pause' develops between the exhalation and inhalation. In a very healthy breather this natural pause may be around three seconds. The next breath will be small, smooth and slow (see Figure 18.1).

To encourage this, see if you can experience this small relaxed 'stillness' (pause) before your next in-breath arrives. Try sitting in the stillness for a moment, before you want to breathe again. Don't grab for the next breath – let it simply 'arrive'. (The natural pause is introduced on Track 4 of the Breathing Exercise Instruction Audio. See the Learning Resources: Audio aids to learning, page 201.)

FIGURE 18.1: HIBERNATION AND THE NATURAL PAUSE

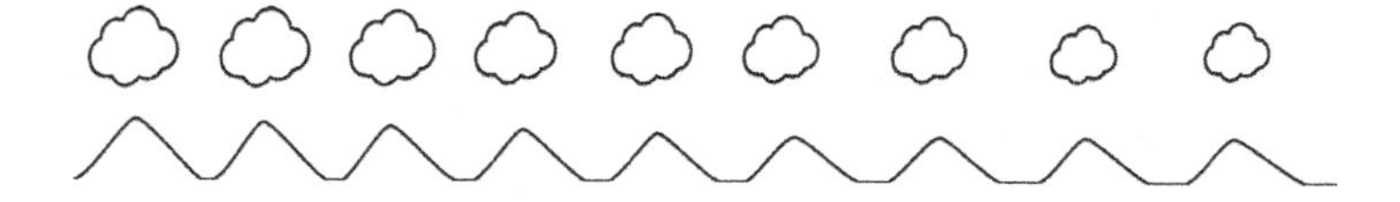

HOW DOES YOUR BREATHING FEEL NOW?

The breathing retraining instructions in the last seven chapters are aimed at bringing the rhythm, rate and volume of air that you breathe back to normal levels. To help you breathe the way you were always meant to, just as a healthy baby does – silently, gently, effortlessly through your nose, with a small movement at the solar plexus level.

If you followed all the steps correctly, then you should be feeling calmer and more relaxed. Hopefully tonight you will sleep peacefully. Would you snore or toss and turn fretfully if your breathing was slow, soft and gentle? I have lost count of the number of times I have heard this comment: 'I was breathing so quietly last night that my husband/wife had to prod me to see if I was still alive.'

If you have had decades of dysfunctional breathing, you may still feel a lot more breathing movement than I have described in these pages. Remember, you are a work in progress!

The first step is awareness of your poor breathing habits, and then step by step you *gently* and *consistently* change them.

Check your heart rate

When you are not pushed for time, check your heart rate before practice and around a minute after you finish it. If you have done the breathing correctly, your pulse rate should reduce, or at least stay the same.

If your heart rate goes up, you are probably not relaxed and/or not breathing correctly – your body is under stress. Adjust your technique or the timing of practice as necessary, for example, not straight after a meal; not when you are hurrying to get out the door.

Also check and record your heart rate on waking each morning. As night-time and general breathing improve, it is usual to see average resting heart rates decrease and then level out into a lower range. Seeing a rise in morning heart rate can be an early indicator of illness, developing a cold, increased stress, or over-breathing. Then you have an opportunity to take some measures to look after yourself. Forewarned may help you to be forearmed.

SIMILARITY TO BREATHING DURING MEDITATION

People who undergo breathing retraining and achieve near-perfect breathing may find that their breathing becomes almost unnoticeable when they sit quietly and focus on it. They may experience a blissful feeling of complete relaxation of mind and body – similar to that experienced during deep meditation and transcendence. It is as though the nervous system perceives the absence of any sympathetic fight-or-flight response and switches progressively to the parasympathetic mode, with deepening relaxation of both the mind and the muscles.

People who have struggled with meditation because they have not been able to quieten the 'monkey mind' often find the meditative state easier to achieve after breathing retraining.

Finding your rhythm

With perfect breathing, the wave pattern is smooth and regular. The exhalation is a little longer than the inhalation. There is the natural, automatic pause of up to three seconds between the out-breath and the next in-breath.

If you follow the guidelines I have given for better breathing, your breathing should evolve towards this ideal. As with respiration rate, you should not force your breathing into the ideal pattern – you let it find its own way there.

ACTION STEPS FOR SILENT, 'INVISIBLE' BREATHING

- Sit in the coathanger posture.
- Breathe smoothly and gently through your nose and with your diaphragm.
- Practise hibernating.
- *Sit in the stillness* before the next breath.
- Breathe 'invisibly, almost as if you are not breathing.
- Practise three times a day, 5–20 minutes total each session.

When to move on

You can move on tomorrow to Healthy Habit Eight: Breathing control during speech and singing. You certainly need more practice with 'silent invisible breathing', but you can do that each day as you learn the next two habits.

CHAPTER 19

Healthy habit eight: Breathing control when speaking and singing

Yes, something as automatic as the way you breathe when you speak plays a role in your breathing and health. Improving your breathing pattern during speech can help you normalise your breathing and reduce your symptoms much faster than if you fail to tackle this issue. And if you speak professionally, you can become a better speaker by having great breath control, and also avoid that horror – stage fright.

PUBLIC SPEAKING ANXIETY

You are up on stage, or it's your turn to speak at a meeting. Your hands and voice are shaking, you're sweating and your heart is racing.

Fear of public speaking, or 'stage fright' or performance anxiety, is so common in the general population that it's even got a fancy name – *glossophobia*. And there is a list of medications to treat it. These include traditional anti-anxiety drugs such as benzodiazepines, antidepressants and beta-blockers. Drugs can seem to be effective in the short term, but they are definitely not a cure. They do not treat the underlying cause; they only mask the symptoms. Once you stop taking them, all the symptoms of stage fright return in full force.

Like other forms of anxiety, over-breathing underlies this condition and so it makes sense to deal with it.

PROBLEMS CAUSED BY POOR BREATHING DURING SPEECH

Talking and singing can make you dehydrated, breathless and congested. It can trigger coughing and tire you out. These symptoms are all precipitated or aggravated by over-breathing and difficulty coordinating breathing and talking.

Are your symptoms worse after a long day of meetings or presentations? Do you need to drink gallons when you talk a lot?

If you are an over-breather, presenting to an audience can also bring on fear and all those symptoms of stage fright. As well as the ones already mentioned, you may get dizzy, feel nauseated, go 'weak at the knees', or even go blank. Stage fright includes symptoms of hyperventilation and acute carbon dioxide deficit!

The quick, gasping upper-chest breaths that people take during speech, generally at the beginning of a sentence, dehydrate and strain the throat. If you have a personality or a job where you talk a lot and this is the way you speak, then you are inadvertently doing a lot of over-breathing. Those who need to talk a lot, like teachers, lawyers, lecturers, tour guides, and salespeople may also develop a chronic cough.

Awareness – observe yourself

To change, you need to recognise the problem. Your family and friends may be more aware of gasping inhales and breathlessness in your speech pattern than you are. Ask for their feedback. You can also try standing in front of a mirror and observe yourself as you recite a poem or tell a story.

Do you talk right to the very end of your out-breath and then gulp the air in quickly and audibly through your mouth? Can you see your shoulders or chest lift?

You can also increase your awareness by watching and listening when others are talking and singing. See if you can spot the poor breathers on television, or when listening to talkback or songs on the radio. Notice the different breathing patterns and noises. With some people you will hear only the words; with others you will hear sharp intakes of breath. This can be particularly obvious over the phone.

GOOD BREATHING DURING SPEECH AND SINGING

It is not the lung capacity, the force and the volume of air that is important in talking and singing. Rather it is the *control* of the air. It is air passing over the vocal cords on the out-breath that makes the 'voice' and only a little air is needed to set them vibrating. The less breath you use, the better the tone. The key then is to be a relaxed, efficient breather.

Australian opera singer Dame Nellie Melba wrote in her book *The Melba Method*, "if only a little breath is necessary, it is obviously wise not to take too much air into the lungs".[19.1] The American singer Frank Sinatra had legendary breath control. He sang with a long relaxed breath; his singing sounded effortless. You could not hear him take a breath, and it was hard to see it happen.

Taking the breath in through your nose is an excellent way to control the air intake. It also engages your diaphragm, which in turn controls the outflowing of air over the vocal cords. The chest and shoulders should not lift. Slowing down your speech calms you.

Benefits of improved breathing in speech and singing include:

- better voice projection
- richer voice tone
- less mucus accumulation in the back of your throat
- less dehydration after presentations and performances
- less fatigue at the end of a day of talking
- greater endurance with singing
- less breathlessness and coughing
- remaining calm while making speeches or performing.

There is also a carry-over effect from improved control of breathing during speech – your general breathing and health improve faster.

Head, neck, body posture during speech

Your posture is also important to speaking. It is the *upright relaxed coathanger posture*. The instructions to 'relax your throat, relax your tongue, loosen your throat' will help you release any tension in your throat that interferes with your voice.

Glenn, an author, came to see me before his latest book was launched. From his past experiences, he was anxious that his voice might not hold up for the book readings his publisher required of him. In our lessons, he became aware of the amount of tension he carried in his throat. The issues around voice and breathing greatly improved once he learnt to 'trust the coathanger', 'stay loose' and hold his head up without tensing and effort from his neck or throat muscles.

STRATEGIES TO BREATHE WELL DURING SPEECH

Having already made the changes suggested in this book so far, you should now be in a better position to control your breathing during speech. The following strategies and exercises are designed to help you develop a speech–breathing pattern where you breathe in through your nose when you need air and maintain good breath control and voice projection.

When you first make these changes, you need to slow down your speech and pause momentarily while closing your mouth, then take that next inhale through your nose. Avoid taking quick upper-chest gasps through your mouth and speaking in long sentences that make you breathless.

Take the in-breaths at the natural 'punctuation' points. Your speech needs punctuation, like full stops and commas, just as your writing does. Punctuation in speech is when you breathe.

Instructions when speaking

1. Have a relaxed, upright posture.
2. Relax your jaw, throat, shoulders, breathing muscles, and stomach.
3. Take a small in-breath through your nose.
4. Allow it into your lungs.
5. Speak slowly.
6. Shorten your sentences until you are more efficient and have better control.
7. When you need another breath, pause for a moment; close your mouth.
8. Take the next small in-breath silently through your nose.
9. Then continue to speak.
10. Practise by reading aloud, or doing the alphabet exercise (see below).

The alphabet exercise

This involves saying the alphabet aloud, using four gentle, silent nasal in-breaths followed by silent, effortless breathing. Figure 19.1 shows where the pauses and in-breaths are.

The critical factors:

- All the in-breaths are small, silent and through the nose.
- At the end of the alphabet (or sentence during normal conversation) you are gently and silently nose breathing.
- There must be no sign of breathlessness afterwards.

FIGURE 19.1: THE ALPHABET EXERCISE

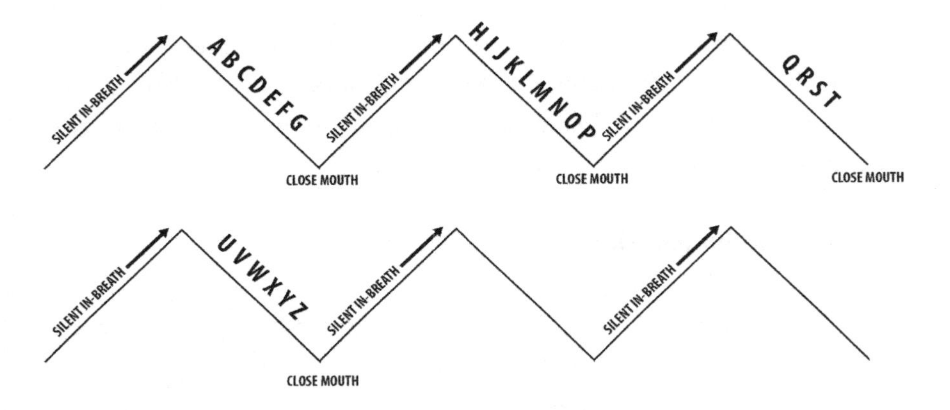

When your breathing has improved, you will be able to say the alphabet in two breaths (A–N, and O–Z). Later on, you may get through the whole alphabet in one breath.

Your speech may be slow and somewhat stilted in the beginning. You may sound like you are delivering the Queen's Christmas message. (Interestingly, clients say that people seem to take more notice of them when they talk this way!) With practice and better breathing you become more fluent. When you speak and breathe well, your pauses for breath won't be noticed.

Correct breathing is very efficient – it's hard to interrupt a good breather, as they do not run out of breath and never seem to pause.

Singing exercise

Try singing the alphabet or the well-known 'happy birthday' song using four silent nasal in-breaths to sing the four phrases. You will see that just a small amount of air is enough to support those phrases.

TALKING AND WALKING

Until you have made significant improvements in your baseline breathing and your control during speech, it is best not to talk too much while you are exercising.

LAUGHTER

Is laughter the best medicine? Not for those who mean it when they say, 'I nearly died laughing'.

While generally very good for us, laughter involves repeated extra-deep breaths and can produce coughing spasms and asthma symptoms. Over 50 per cent of asthmatics report that laughter can provoke symptoms. It is important for those with breathing problems to try to maintain a level of control during laughter.

Instructions when laughing

Take the in-breaths through your nose if you can. Between bouts of laughter, recover with nose breathing. It may help to do a couple of short breath holds – two to three seconds, to replenish your carbon dioxide after laughing.

ACTION STEPS FOR BREATH CONTROL IN SPEECH, SINGING AND LAUGHING

- Become self-aware.
- Take the in-breaths through your nose when speaking, singing and laughing.
- Speak slowly; shorten your sentences.
- Punctuate your speech with brief pauses.
- Practise speaking or singing in front of a mirror.
- Practise the alphabet exercise or reading aloud.
- Control your breathing during and after laughing.
- Use short breath holds if necessary to recover from laughing.

CHAPTER 20

Healthy habit nine: Breathing well during exercise

Regular physical exercise not only promotes physical health but is also good for your mental health. Many studies have linked inactivity to higher levels of anxiety.

It is well known that exercise burns stress hormones, releases endorphins (happy brain hormones) and boosts your mood. A walk, a bike ride or whatever exercise you enjoy can discharge the fight-or-flight response because it uses up the excess adrenaline and glucose in the blood. Exercising as soon as possible when the stress occurs is best, but it can still be beneficial within a couple of hours. By reducing the stress chemicals in your body, you reduce the risk of developing stress-related diseases. Those who exercise regularly are generally calmer and more productive than those who don't.

Many people today, however, are too busy or too tired to exercise, and the typical day involves little movement – drive to work, sit at a desk for eight to ten hours, drive home, sit in front of the television, and lie down in bed. We move less in a day than did our forebears, who had to chop wood, wash clothes by hand, work on the land, and walk to markets and social gatherings.

Exercise conundrum

A sedentary lifestyle and a lack of exercise can indeed be detrimental to your health. Conversely, however, exercise can cause or exacerbate certain health problems and even bring on various symptoms and ailments. We have all heard of exercise-induced asthma and exercise-induced heart attacks. Overtraining and exercise done with poor breathing can actually stress your adrenals and have detrimental effects on your mental and physical health. The key to healthy exercise is to breathe well. And the master key is nose breathing.

You can't look at the average elite athlete as an example of the best way to breathe during exercise, or at rest for that matter. Athletes suffer more than their fair share of respiratory illnesses and may experience burn-out, anxiety, fatigue, and immune dysfunction due to pushing their bodies to the limit – while breathing inefficiently. Having an Olympic gold medal does not necessarily mean you have optimal breathing.

By taking the principles of correct breathing into exercise, you can improve not only your fitness and the safety and enjoyment of exercise, but also more quickly improve and recondition your breathing.

THE TARAHUMARA RUNNERS

These legendary endurance runners from the Copper Canyon in northern Mexico live in a hot environment with steep canyons. They run up to 120 km a day. Legend has it that the Tarahumara can run non-stop for three days and three nights. To hunt deer, they chase it on foot until the deer is exhausted. To them, running is a way of life. The secret to their amazing ability that has stunned researchers is said to be that they traditionally breathe only through the nose.

Do the opposite – push your breathing and blood chemistry further from normal as you exercise – and you may pay for it by worsening your baseline breathing, increasing your symptoms and possibly introducing new ones.

BREATHING CHANGES DURING EXERCISE

When exercising, you need to breathe more than when resting. But you don't need to do it on purpose. Your working muscles need more oxygen, and they produce more carbon dioxide; increased carbon dioxide naturally stimulates breathing. The greater the intensity of exercise, the more your breathing will deepen. During prolonged intensive exercise you may breathe 10 times more air per minute than at rest.

How do you know you have it right? It feels good. No stress. (And not much sweat, literally!)

HEALTHY BREATHING DURING EXERCISE

Healthy breathing during exercise is breathing in and out through the nose, using the diaphragm efficiently. Inhaling through the nose ensures filtering, humidification and warming of the air. Exhaling through the nose also helps maintain hydration of the nasal tissues and sinuses. Nose breathing during exercise is perfectly natural. It is possible and comfortable *when your baseline breathing pattern is right.*

For excellent breathers, only very high-intensity exercise may require mouth breathing – for example, during repeated 'explosive' sprints in football. Even then they quickly recover and soon switch back to relaxed nose breathing. It's hard to find a nose breathing runner in western cultures, but check out a horse race – those majestic creatures run their heavy bodies at such speed and over such long distances, while breathing through their noses. (The jockey may have his mouth open.)

In healthy people, respiration rate should not need to go above 16 breaths a minute during aerobic-type exercise, like brisk walking, walking up hills or jogging. It is better to get the increased minute volume you need through a *moderate* increase in the *number* of breaths per minute and a *significant* increase in the *amount* of air in each breath. This is achieved through proper breathing rhythm and diaphragm action. This breathing pattern is very different from what I observe in the average social exerciser and the elite athlete (see Table 20.1 below).

TABLE 20.1: BREATHING DURING MILD TO MODERATE EXERCISE

Healthy breathing	Poor breathing
Nose breathing	Mouth breathing
Diaphragm breathing	Upper-chest breathing
16 or fewer breaths/minute	25+ breaths/minute
Quiet or moderately audible breathing	Noisy, heavy, gasping breathing

POOR BREATHING DURING EXERCISE

This is typically through the mouth, excessively fast and over-involves the upper-chest breathing muscles. These muscles consume a lot more energy than the diaphragm and they fatigue easily. Rapid breathing also doesn't allow time to oxygenate the blood adequately and contributes to breathlessness and early fatigue. Another fault is to forcefully exhale (with or without a grunt) as much air as possible – usually through the mouth.

The consequences of over-breathing during exercise include:

- dehydration of airways
- overproduction of mucus
- less oxygen available to organs and tissues (Bohr effect)
- lactic acid accumulation in muscles
- angina
- asthma
- shortness of breath
- performance anxiety.

After years of encouragement to breathe deeply, fully and forcefully during sports and fitness sessions, Ella found that by practising relaxed 'lower' volume diaphragm breathing, exercise felt less stressful, she could exercise for longer without fatiguing and she recovered faster.

Exercise professionals and amateurs alike are obsessed with the myth that taking in heaps of oxygen and pushing out as much carbon dioxide as possible is healthy. In fact, forced over-breathing causes blood vessels to constrict and oxygen molecules to cling tightly to the red blood cells. This results in insufficient oxygen being available to the muscles and everywhere else. Breathlessness, fatigue and lactic acid build-up follow.

Have you noticed the distress some 'fitness fanatics' are in after an intensive cardio session at the gym, or athletes during and at the finish of events? Red in the face, sweating profusely, muscles tight and cramping, mouth wide open, sucking in the air but seemingly unable to get enough. (Stretcher-bearers are often on standby at the end of endurance events.) By contrast, the Tarahumara are observed to have a look of peacefulness on their faces and ease in their bodies after completing a long run.

Does it still sound impossible to jog, run or cycle with your mouth shut? What seems impossible now can change once you have improved your baseline breathing enough. When you are an efficient breather, you get by comfortably with a lot less air, and the amount available with nose breathing becomes sufficient – as it is for the Tarahumara, and is it was for the Kenyan distance runners in times past.

BENEFITS OF BETTER BREATHING DURING EXERCISE

Frequently reported benefits following breathing retraining include:

- easier breathing
- greater endurance
- energised after exercise
- less dehydration and need for fluids
- less need for asthma reliever medication
- less lactic acid, cramping and muscle soreness
- faster recovery
- lower heart rate for same intensity exercise (see Table 20.2).

TABLE 20.2: TYPICAL HEART RATE CHANGES WITH BREATHING RETRAINING

	Before	Day five
Average heart rate at rest	78	63 (19% reduction)
Average heart rate after two- minute medium pace walk	91	67 (26% reduction)
Heart rate 60 secs after 400m sprint (elite athlete)	130	70 (46% reduction)

CARBON DIOXIDE – A PERFORMANCE-ENHANCING 'DRUG'

I have seen breathing retraining produce phenomenal improvement in social exercisers, professional athletes and Olympic champions. So dramatic have the results been at times that the athletes have been asked by their coaches the reason for their sudden 'performance enhancement'. This is carbon dioxide acting like a performance-enhancing drug! It enhances oxygen delivery to the working muscles. It is not a banned substance – it is meant to show up in your bloodstream. But when exercise looks too easy, people can get suspicious.

At interschool cross-country events, parents and teachers are used to seeing the competing children red in the face, sweaty, doubled up with stitches and stomach cramps, and even vomiting at the finish line. At one such event, my 10-year-old son came into sight and sprinted to the finish line a good 50m in front of the next runner. His mouth was shut, his breathing was calm and quiet. I overheard one of the teachers from another school say to our headmaster, "That boy must have taken a shortcut," and the headmaster replied, "No way, not this kid, but I know his mother does something funny with breathing."

STRATEGIES FOR BREATHING WELL DURING EXERCISE

You are ready to work on improving your breathing during physical exercise if your breathing is generally quieter, slower and more controlled than it used to be, and if you now breathe comfortably through your nose and with your diaphragm (most of the time at least), including when you are walking. If not, spend more time practising these habits or seek help from a breathing educator.

Increasing your daily exercise can be as simple as walking to the shops, parking the car further from the office or taking the stairs rather than the lift. It is also important to find a type of exercise that you enjoy.

Begin with an activity and intensity that you are used to, and that is relaxed and rhythmical, like walking, riding a stationary exercise bike or jogging. Start on the flat.

Be led by your nose

Let your nose dictate the pace of your exercise. That is, don't exercise to the point where you have to open your mouth. As you improve, gradually increase your pace, distance or the gradient.

If your nose starts to block up or drip, or you begin to puff or feel breathless, then you are moving too fast for your current breathing status. Your breathing fitness is not yet up to your leg fitness.

Let's think of the golden rule again: *Go only as fast as your nose will comfortably allow.*

GET CHECKED

If you are sedentary, unfit, over 40, or suffer from chronic health problems such as heart disease, asthma, COPD, diabetes, or obesity, you should consult your doctor before beginning an exercise program or substantially changing one. If you have been unwell or inactive for some time, it is important to start slowly and build up at a comfortable rate.

And you can add to it: *Go slow now to be faster later.*

Maintain coathanger posture and use your diaphragm well

Exercise as though you have your coathanger in position, relaxing and dropping your shoulders, lengthening your body upwards through your head as you are moving forwards – walking/running tall. As you do this, your breathing eases and centres on your diaphragm. By keeping your stomach muscles relaxed, your diaphragm can move freely and efficiently, adapting to any increased requirements for air.

As you go up a hill, it moves through a larger amplitude, naturally drawing in more air per breath. This also allows your ribs to move as nature intended. Your whole soft gold band area will expand more. Tell yourself, 'relax and expand the band'.

For the out-breath, as always, let it be passive. Think of the exhalation simply *falling out* and the next breath arriving in its own time. Relax into your natural rhythm.

When you go downhill, your air requirement reduces, and so will your chest expansion. There is little upper-chest involvement in mild and moderate intensity exercise.

The golden rules here are:

The more intense the exercise, the more your soft gold band expands (see Figure 20.1).

Stay comfortable and in control.

Bronwyn had been training on the same hill for years, always getting aching legs within five minutes of starting up the hill. Using her diaphragm properly and keeping her respiration rate below 16 breaths saw the end of the aching legs.

FIGURE 20.1: BREATHING DURING EXERCISE

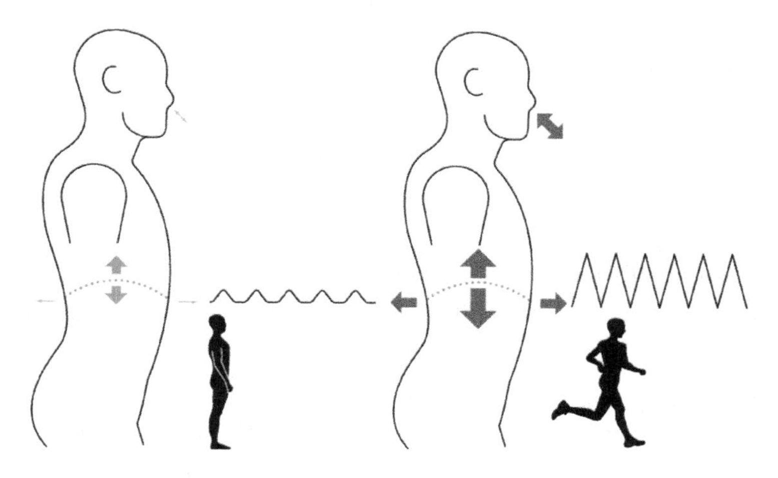

Recovery

After a warm-down recovery period, spend five minutes focusing on relaxed nose-diaphragm breathing. Your breathing rate will gradually decrease to your resting rate. This will also help bring your heart rate back towards resting rate.

PRACTICE SET: NOSE-DIAPHRAGM BREATHING DURING EXERCISE

1. Choose a mild to moderate aerobic and continuous-motion type exercise.
2. Practice relaxed nose-diaphragm breathing for two minutes before starting.
3. Start out at a slower pace (initially).
4. Maintain the relaxed, lengthened coathanger posture.
5. Breathe in and out through your nose.
6. Breathe with a relaxed diaphragm motion.
7. Have a soft stomach.
8. Allow the soft gold band/diaphragm area to expand on the in-breath.
9. Allow your back to be breathed.
10. Let go on the out-breath.
11. Allow deeper, fuller breaths as your need increases.
12. Find your natural rhythm for breathing and stepping.

13. Do not strain.
14. Gradually increase your pace/gradient as your comfort allows.
15. Control your breathing during warm-down and recovery.
16. Practise relaxed nose-diaphragm breathing for five minutes after warm-down.

PRACTICE TIMES

Build up gradually to a total of 30 minutes' exercise a day, four to six times a week if appropriate. The 30 minutes does not have to be done in one go.

Note: When your aim is to improve your breathing pattern, it is best to immediately reduce your pace, or stop, the moment you feel any symptoms or indications of pain or discomfort, rather than pushing yourself to the point where you have to open your mouth to breathe.

Remember: Comfortable and in control.

Timing of exercise

Exercising in the evening can increase the level of cortisol. When cortisol is raised, melatonin is suppressed. Melatonin is one of the primary growth and repair hormones and it is also the hormone that sends you off to sleep. This is why it is recommended not to exercise two to three hours before going to bed.

MAKING PROGRESS

Increase your speed, distance and the incline gradually as your breathing and fitness improve.

When you first exercise with nose breathing, it can be difficult to keep pace with someone else or carry on a conversation. Either walk alone until you have your rhythm and control, or let the other person know that you won't be as fast or chatty as usual. Otherwise you could find yourself mouth breathing and hyperventilating.

Once you have your 'nose-diaphragm rhythm' you can try other forms of exercise like rowing, gardening or dancing; then the less rhythmic forms like tennis.

If, like most people, you have been exercising with your mouth open all your life, then you are going to have some unlearning and reconditioning to do. Initially when switching to nose breathing, you will get a drop in performance but soon notice that you will be able to perform at your previous level or higher, with a lower heart rate and a much lower perceived intensity. It may take weeks to work up to it, but eventually nose-diaphragm breathing can be the norm.

My youngest son had been joining me on an early morning riverbank run from the age of five. He had only ever known nose breathing when running. At the age of 12, he started at a new school. The sports teacher was watching 'the new talent' during the various events at the athletics carnival. Tom had already won the 100, 200 and 400 m races. Now he was running the 1,500 m. As he effortlessly ran the laps of the oval, the sports teacher must have thought Tom was not actually trying, not giving his all. He looked too laid-back compared to the other boys who were 'really' trying – gulping for air, red in the face or struggling with a stitch. As Tom passed him on the second, third and final laps, the teacher yelled out each time, "Open your mouth!" Tom didn't. He won the race easily.

I knew the teacher's instruction would have been very embarrassing and disconcerting for my son. I said to him afterwards that I hoped he hadn't ignored the teacher just because he knew I was watching. Tom's response was, "No, I tried to open my mouth but I just couldn't work out how to do it."

It is important to get nose-diaphragm breathing second nature during low intensity exercise, before you adapt it into intensive or competitive exercise. Breath size and rate both need to increase as intensity increases. When you have normal baseline breathing, your nose can cope with a substantial further increase in both.

ADVANCED TRAINING

The work I do with athletes begins the same as with anyone else – they improve their baseline breathing first (sitting, watching TV). Then they apply the principles during activity, then while walking, and then jogging, running, cycling, rowing, swimming, and so on. After four days on an intensive breathing retraining course, athletes are usually ready to apply more advanced breathing techniques during training at the gym, field, track, or pool, and with more vigorous physical exertion. I was never surprised when they called me to report personal bests less than two weeks later. (Such intensive, individualised, guided and fine-tuned training, and the targeted application for specific sports, is beyond the scope of this book.)

ACTION STEPS FOR BREATHING WELL DURING EXERCISE AND SPORT

- Introduce nose–diaphragm breathing into an aerobic exercise routine.
- Go slower initially.
- Exercise within your capability.
- Gradually increase your pace as your breathing improves.
- Control your breathing during warm-down and recovery.

The golden rules

- Go only as fast as your nose will comfortably allow.
- Go slow now to be faster later.
- The more intense the exercise, the more your soft gold band expands.
- Be comfortable and in control.

CHAPTER 21

Where to from here?

BEYOND THE FIRST NINE DAYS OR SO

While you can learn all nine habits of healthy breathing within nine days, you may not yet have completely normalised your breathing. You may have come a long way from where you started, but it's important to further improve and consolidate the changes.

You can achieve this by being mindful of your breathing throughout the day and by continuing for a while with daily practice sessions. One of the best ways to maintain and further improve your breathing is to do physical exercise with good breathing.

Blending good breathing practice into your life

You can 'hibernate' on the bus or train, or as you queue at the post office or airport. It can be helpful to think of yourself as a work in progress. Hopefully by now you look forward to the 10, 15 or 20-minute practice before bed because of the quality sleep that has become your reward.

I recommend that you continue some formal practice as long as your breathing pattern, energy levels and breathing-related symptoms continue to improve. By being physically active and applying good breathing practices in every aspect of your daily life (informal practice), you should be able to gradually reduce the amount of formal practice you do and not only maintain the improvements you have, but improve further over time. Eventually, healthy breathing can become completely automatic; your default breathing set point will be normal.

You do need though to continue to monitor your breathing, especially in times of physical or emotional stress – and in party season. It's a health insurance check-up. Make use of the additional assessment columns in Table 1.1 (page 6) and 3.1 (pages 24-25) to keep in touch with your breathing.

THE THREE-DAY HOLIDAY

I use the concept of declaring a 'three-day holiday' when I suspect that people have been overly focused on improving their breathing and more or less forcing their body into a new pattern, forcing diaphragm breathing or nose breathing. This causes internal tension and/or physical tension in their chest, shoulders or jaw. It can appear as though the mind and body are fighting back. Rather, what you want, is to stay relaxed about your breathing. Simply and gently undoing bad habits, letting them drop away, and allowing gentler, nose-diaphragm breathing to simply happen. That is, get your over-controlling self out of the way.

A solution I have found that has worked brilliantly each time is to 'forbid' any formal practice or focused attention on breathing for at least three days. If it's someone attending classes, I will even hold on to their course notes and recording sheets during this period so they are not tempted to practise on the 'holiday'.

If this speaks to you, my reader, put away this book now, and come back in three days or so. Then do some formal practice again if it feels good. Don't worry, you will not resume all those bad habits by having a break – you may in fact have a *breakthrough*. If not, see a breathing educator for advice. Also, see Chapter 25.

HELP FOR PSYCHOLOGICAL PROBLEMS

Resolve emotional and personal issues by talking to a counsellor or psychologist and access support systems in the community. With a normal breathing pattern, you are more likely able to process these issues contributing to your anxiety relatively quickly.

MINDFULNESS

A worthy companion to breathing control is training in mindfulness – a practice of living in and accepting the present moment. Your awareness of self and of your breathing developed through breathing retraining leads naturally into increased mindfulness. Each benefits the other.

SELF-CARE

Allocate time for rest, relaxation, exercise, and being with friends. Balance is something we struggle with in our current modern world. We need life, work, family, friends, meaning, health, and wellbeing. We never achieve all we can by getting the balance wrong.

HEALING RESPONSE

Reducing over-breathing results in an enhanced *parasympathetic (relaxation) response* in the body. The nervous system and the musculoskeletal system 'relax'. When there is release of neuromuscular tension, there may also be an emotional release. It's comforting for those who experience this during breathing retraining sessions to know how natural it is and what it means – progress! Take it easy, be gentle on yourself, get support if you need it, and look and move forward to a brighter future.

Some people experience a temporary 'revisit' of some symptoms that have long been issues for them, such as mucus discharge, tiredness, niggling aches and pains. It seems like the body is letting go of physical stuff as well. If you have any doubt or concerns, see your healthcare professional.

If symptoms return

You need to start the exercises again if you notice a return of signs and symptoms – for example, during a stressful period or illness. This is where referring back to your Breathing Pattern Self-Assessment (page 6) and Dysfunctional Breathing Symptom Tracker (page 24) can prove valuable. You may prevent this situation from happening in the future if you identify and address any triggers or lifestyle factors responsible for deterioration in your breathing, and if you continue to improve your baseline breathing pattern and recondition your breathing set point. A list of factors that can slow your progress or be responsible for a return of symptoms is in Chapter 25.

If your anxiety is complicated by other illnesses, or your improvements fall short of the ideal, it is recommended you work with a proficient breathing educator. (See Chapter 26.)

CHAPTER 22

Rescue breathing exercises for anxiety and panic attacks

In this chapter, I provide some 'panic control' exercises that are useful to quickly reduce anxiety or quell a panic attack. They can also help with emotional shock or stage fright, breathlessness, racing mind, or racing heart. They can be used anywhere, anytime and require no equipment.

These exercises use a sequence of short breath holds, [illegible] They act as a 'pattern interrupt', to interrupt a rapid, forceful or panicky over-breathing pattern that has decreased carbon dioxide, revved up your nervous system and pushed you into a fight-or-flight response. Of course, by correcting your everyday baseline breathing, in the long term you will prevent anxiety and panic and have less need for these strategies. Even if you cannot eliminate all the stresses in your world, you can change your body's response.

THE PANIC CONTROL EXERCISES

'3 x 3' and '3-to-5-and-back-again' versions

Both versions of panic control exercises help retain and gently accumulate carbon dioxide to:

- slow and calm your breathing
- deactivate the fight-or-flight response
- calm you.

INSTRUCTIONS

3 x 3

1. Pause your breath for a count of three (one to three seconds).

2. Breathe again, in and out, in and out...as slowly and gently as you comfortably can for three breaths.
3. Repeat steps 1 and 2 until relief is felt, or for five minutes, whichever comes first (see Figure 22.1A.)

3-to-5-and-back-again (progression version)

4. As your breathing eases, you can progress from pauses of a count of three, to pauses of a count of four, then five, repeating each length of pause twice. Then you work the pattern back down again – pauses of a count of four, then three. (Figure 22.1B.)

Rules

As always with short breath holds, you must avoid pausing your breath for so long that you need a larger inhalation afterwards or have any breathlessness. This is counterproductive. Don't repeat the sequence of short breath holds too quickly – allow at least three breaths in between each pause.

FIGURE 22.1: PANIC CONTROL EXERCISES

A: 3 X 3

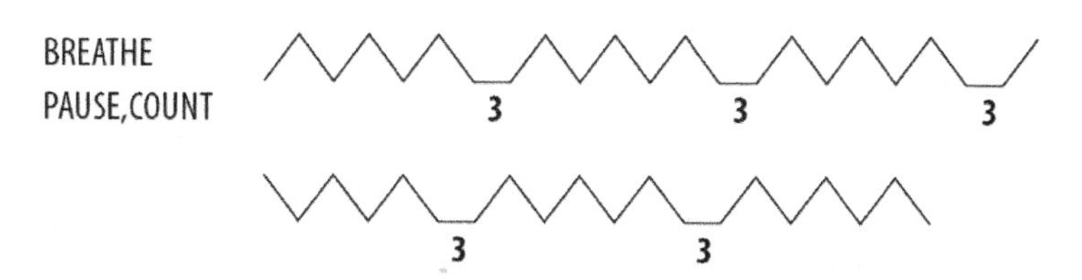

B: 3 TO 5 AND BACK AGAIN

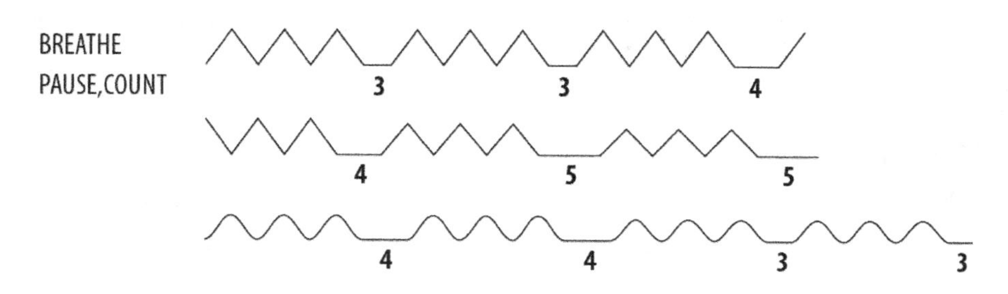

These simple exercises interrupt a pattern of relentless (but still possibly invisible) over-breathing. They enable you to get to a quiet place, to gather yourself, a benefit of raising your carbon dioxide just a little.

I had not yet met Henry but I had spoken to him a few days earlier when he phoned to book a consultation. When he called again he was very distressed, in fact suicidal. Over the phone I could hear his rapid breaths and the panic in his voice. He was not only severely distressed but dizzy and confused. No time for explanations, I asked him to simply follow my voice and told him that I would check with him soon about how he was doing. I said I would introduce short pauses into his breathing with the words, "Pause two, three" (about one second to start with). I listened for the ins and outs of Henry's breathing and introduced the short pauses every three to five breaths.

After about eight cycles I could no longer hear him breathing and I added, "Now try to breathe through your nose if you have not already switched over to it. Breathe as softly as you can. Now, how are you feeling?" The answer was "Amazing!" Henry said that he felt completely calm, his heart had stopped thumping and his breathing had freed up. Even I was amazed at the power of the short breath holds, and yet I had seen many times before the look of wonder and relief on people's faces after coaching them through panic attacks. Henry then went on to get the help he needed from me and others.

In an acute situation like a panic attack, initially just focus on slowing down your breathing by introducing the small pauses. Don't worry at first about nose breathing, good posture and your diaphragm – once you are feeling calmer you can give them attention. While it is best to use the pauses with nose breathing, they can still be helpful with mouth breathing, or a combination of the two. You can pause your breathing anywhere in the cycle, although it is preferable after the exhale.

reasons. One, they are distracted; two, it uses up some of the extra adrenaline and creates more carbon dioxide because muscles are active. Similarly, many people find stress relief from a brisk walk.

INSTRUCTIONS

While walking:

1. Breathe in and out naturally, as you walk, for about a minute.
2. After a natural out-breath, pause your breathing while you walk two steps/paces.
3. Repeat this sequence…breathing, walking for about a minute… pause your breathing for two steps.
4. Then after breathing naturally again as you walk for about a minute, pause your breathing over three steps.
5. Repeat the sequence, then move on to pausing your breathing for four steps.
6. Repeat this…breathing, walking a minute…pause breathing for four steps.
7. Now work the sequence down again, in reverse, until you arrive back at pausing your breathing as you walk for two steps.

Rules

When you breathe again after a pause, control your breathing, keep it as calm and gentle as you can without discomfort. Do not hold your breath for so long that it causes stress, any negative reaction or an over-breathing response. If you notice a larger inhalation afterwards or any breathlessness, go down to a lower pause level in the sequence. You should feel comfortable and in control on the first breath of each level.

It is best if all breathing is nose breathing.

VISUALISING THE CLOUD

Others have found relief simply by breathing more gently, visualising a very gradual shrinking of their 'cloud', or even cupping their hands over their mouth and nose. You could also use the hibernation exercise learnt in Chapter 18.

PANIC ATTACKS IN BED

The best strategies here are to:

- sit up and support yourself with pillows
- relax your breathing muscles
- try the 3 x 3 and /or 3-to-5-and-back-again exercise, or
- get up and walk about (or do the therapeutic walk page 162).

Some people find a hot water bottle against their solar plexus helpful.

The fabulous thing about these breathing strategies is that they can be done anywhere, any time; they are not dependent on a particular environment or a piece of equipment. The tools are truly within you.

ACTION STEPS FOR RELIEF OF ANXIETY AND PANIC ATTACKS

Prevention

- Practise the 3 x 3, 3-to-5-and-back-again or therapeutic walk version of short breath holds for five minutes, twice a day, for three days, to familiarise yourself with them. Then you have a tool ready should you need it.
- Work towards bringing your baseline breathing pattern as close to normal breathing as you can, to reduce the likelihood of anxiety symptoms or a panic attack.
- Seek whatever help you need from a mental health professional.

Emergency procedure

The list below includes the rescue breathing exercises as well as additional strategies you may find helpful.

1. Control your breathing, using:
   - 3 x 3 or 3-to-5-and-back-again exercise for 5–10 minutes
   - therapeutic walk
   - visualisation and gently 'shrinking your cloud'
   - hibernation exercise.
2. Retreat. Remove yourself from the situation if you can until the sensations die down, or relieve them with the above strategies.
3. Get help or reassurance from others.

4. Follow the advice or use techniques you have learnt from a doctor, psychologist or counsellor.
5. Use up your extra adrenaline and create more carbon dioxide by being active – move around, go for a brisk walk in a safe environment.

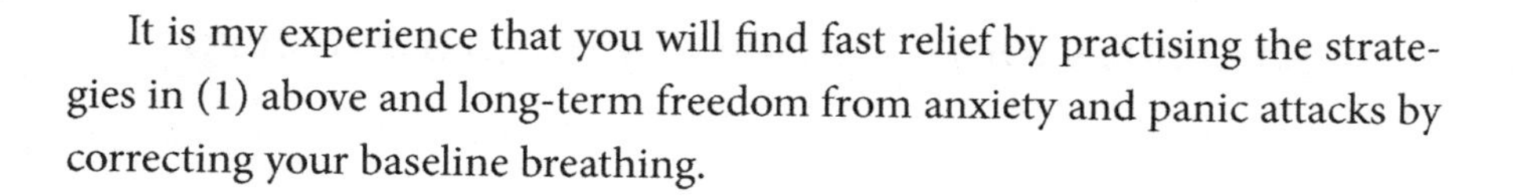

It is my experience that you will find fast relief by practising the strategies in (1) above and long-term freedom from anxiety and panic attacks by correcting your baseline breathing.

Calm your breathing, calm your nervous system, calm your life.

CHAPTER 23

Strategies for insomnia and improved sleep

Disturbed breathing, specifically over-breathing, can contribute to a 'hyper-arousal' state that prevents sleep. By calming your breathing before sleep and creating a slight rise in carbon dioxide, you make use of its sedative effects, inducing your body's relaxation response. This may reduce excessive brain activity, insomnia and nightmares and help you achieve a deeper, more refreshing sleep.

Many clients have successfully used the 3 x 3 exercise (or 3-to-5-and-back-again version) while lying in bed to get off to sleep (see Figure 22.1). They tell me it works better than counting sheep. Even just the practice of gentle diaphragm breathing as you lie in bed may be enough.

You can also use the 3 x 3 exercise if you wake up panicked or you can't get back to sleep. Think of it as deactivating your fight-or-flight response, or like taking a natural sedative.

GOOD SLEEP HABITS – SLEEP HYGIENE

In addition to general improvement in your breathing and use of the 3 x 3 exercise, developing good sleep habits (sleep *hygiene*) can be very helpful.

Regular aerobic exercise, like walking, promotes a better sleeping pattern, although it's best not to do vigorous exercise too close to sleep time because it revs up your metabolism.

You are designed to cycle with the natural cycle of light and darkness. It is best to get up when the sun is rising and fall asleep within three hours of sunset, and to sleep as near as possible in total darkness.

In the interests of calm and relaxation, try not to use electronic devices, computers or television or fluorescent lights in the hour before going to sleep. They stimulate the sympathetic nervous system, causing a rise in cortisol – the awakening hormone – not helpful in falling asleep. It's best to remove LED electronic devices near your bed as these lights and electromagnetic fields interfere with sleep. Overuse of back-lit screen devices at night is also suspected of interfering with sleep by suppressing melatonin.

Having a warm bath or shower before bed may help. As your body cools afterwards when you lie in bed, this entices sleep. Also be aware that an overly warm bedroom temperature or too many bedclothes can cause your body to overheat, leading to over-breathing and poor sleep. To go to sleep and stay asleep your core temperature needs to drop.

Lastly, insomnia may be related to various health conditions and medications, including anxiety and depression and alcohol or drug addiction. It is important to be checked for conditions underlying chronic insomnia and to seek help to manage these difficult issues.

While prescription medications specifically designed for aiding sleep can be helpful for the short term or occasional use, they may be less effective when used regularly and may have side-effects. Modern approaches to sleep are starting to emphasise behavioural approaches rather than pharmaceutical.

ACTION STEPS FOR INSOMNIA RELIEF AND GOOD SLEEP

- Eat your last meal two to three hours before bed, and avoid foods and drinks that elevate your breathing rate.
- Relax in the evening.
- Avoid work, worry or stimulating activities in the evening (no suspense movies).
- Avoid use of computers, other electronic devices and fluorescent lights in the evening; remove LED light electronic devices near your bed.
- Exercise regularly, but not within three hours of bedtime.
- Avoid alcohol and caffeine late in the evening.
- Take a warm shower or bath two hours before bedtime.
- Go to bed and get up around the same time each day.
- Avoid overheating in bed.

- Do 10 minutes of relaxed diaphragm breathing practice before bed.
- Try the 3 x 3 exercise for five to ten minutes, or visualise 'shrinking your cloud' if you have trouble getting to sleep.
- Address any psychological or medical issues that underlie your insomnia.
- Normalise your breathing for the long term.

CHAPTER 24

Working with your doctor

One dilemma we face is that treatment of anxiety disorders is dominated by the medical profession and they have a strong leaning towards pharmaceutical solutions. While drug therapy has saved many lives and treated many illnesses throughout history, and will always be an essential part of medicine, blind adherence to pharmaceutical 'solutions' can result in doctors not being open to non-drug therapies. The many complementary therapists trained and equipped to assist with anxiety disorders using non-drug approaches may not get a look in.

Of course, for many people with anxiety disorders, drugs do provide essential relief from difficult and distressing symptoms. They may however become dependent on these medications to 'dull' their symptoms, and find they have to live with side-effects. It is often the unwanted side-effects and/or the limited effectiveness of pharmaceutical treatments that bring people to non-drug based approaches like breathing retraining. Others who seek out breathing retraining wish to relieve co-existing breathing-related issues like nasal problems, irritable cough, asthma, snoring, or sleep apnoea.

Breathing retraining offers a wonderful opportunity to take back control of your breathing and balance your physiology naturally. It is empowering, but with that power comes responsibility. When you change something as fundamental as the way you breathe, regular monitoring by yourself and your doctor is essential.

CHANGING NEEDS – REAPPRAISAL OF PRESCRIBED TREATMENTS

Participants in breathing retraining programs are requested not to alter or cease medication or other prescribed treatments without the guidance and supervision of their doctor, no matter how well controlled they feel their condition is. If you are working with a breathing educator, they will look at various indicators to make recommendations for the timing of a review. If you are working on your own, your Breathing Pattern Self-assessment (page 6) and Dysfunctional Breathing Symptom Tracker (pages 24-25) can be valuable tools in guiding you when it is time to see your doctor for review.

Your doctor can reassess your condition, monitor the effects of the changes in your breathing pattern and determine your requirements for prescribed treatments if and when necessary.[2] It is ideal if there is communication and collaboration between all health professionals and educators involved in your care.

It is possible that prescribed treatments may no longer be required or a lesser dosage now appropriate. This has been the experience of many people who have learnt to breathe correctly. However, withdrawal or reduction of prescribed treatments needs to be a judicious, medically supervised process. If someone simply drops their medication, or reduces it too quickly, it could cause problems.

Throughout medication withdrawal or decrease, it is very important to continue with improving your breathing and any nutritional, counselling or behavioural therapy you do. Supplements and good nutrition can be a great support during a weaning process.

Twenty-eight-year-old Brooke had suffered for years with asthma, hay fever and severe panic attacks. Her panic attacks could last for hours and it would take her 10 days to recover. She had been on antidepressant medication for over two years and thought it could be forever. Brooke applied what I had taught her and her next panic attack was over in minutes. At a review four months later she reported that everything had improved. Episodes of panic were now rare, very mild, easily controlled through breathing, and she recovered quickly. She had no more palpitations or chest pains, less sweats and dizziness and no lung congestion or asthma symptoms. She was generally a calmer person. Her doctor had reduced her anti-depressants by 80 per cent so far. He commented that Brooke had been seeing him once or twice a week and now it had reduced to three months between visits.

---

2 *Chapter 25 in Relief from Snoring and Sleep Apnoea discusses in depth these issues in relation to sleep apnoea and use of CPAP therapy.*

Take the time to complete another breathing pattern assessment (Table 1.1, page 6), if you haven't already done so. How does your breathing compare to before – nose vs mouth breathing, diaphragm vs upper-chest breathing, and regular vs erratic breathing? Has the frequency of yawning and sighing reduced? What is your respiration rate and resting heart rate now compared to before?

With improvements to your breathing you are less likely to experience sympathetic dominant symptoms like agitation, pounding heart, dry mouth, nervousness, insomnia, or feeling jittery, shaky or spaced out. If any of your symptoms return, ask yourself what has been happening that may have revved your breathing up again. What set off that yawning marathon?

Has there been a change in the amount of mucus, headaches, energy, concentration levels, overnight toilet visits, restless legs, and anxiety? You might also like to complete another assessment column on your Dysfunctional Breathing Symptom Tracker (Table 3.1, pages 24-25).

If your doctor has had little exposure to breathing retraining, it may help a lot if you show him or her your before and after Breathing Pattern Assessments and Dysfunctional Breathing Symptom Tracker when you go for review. They provide a progress report.

Long-term responsibility

Keep in mind that breathing retraining is a self-management approach for breathing dysfunction – not a treatment or cure for anxiety, mood or sleep disorders. Should your breathing pattern deteriorate, your symptoms may return or new symptoms may arise. So continue to close your mouth, breathe gently, sleep on your side, watch your food choices and alcohol consumption and most importantly, mind your breathing.

Stress has a huge impact on breathing. When you are under stress – situations can include job loss, intense physical exertion, grief – your breathing may become deeper and/or faster again, putting you at risk of a return of symptoms. To avoid this, you should keep an eye on your breathing pattern every day, watch out for symptoms and check your heart rate on waking. Then you can take action accordingly to remain symptom-free.

Whatever management or treatment option you have taken, should you be unsuccessful in improving your breathing or if your symptoms get worse or return, see your doctor.

MEDICATIONS FOR OTHER CONDITIONS

Just as your anxiety and mental health require monitoring to adapt treatment to changing needs, so too do any associated conditions such as high blood pressure, heart conditions and diabetes for which medications are prescribed. When your breathing improves, several things may happen:

- Your body may become more efficient at metabolising or excreting a medication.
- Your body may become more sensitive to a medication.
- The body function that the medication is supplementing or replacing may normalise.
- The symptoms that the medication was treating may lessen or be eliminated.

This means that if you substantially change your breathing, there is a possibility that your requirements for medications can change, and research has borne this out.[24.1 –24.3] Therefore, reassessment of all your medication needs by your doctor is very important.

It has long been known that making lifestyle changes can affect the need for medications and treatments. For example, if you are overweight, then losing weight and exercising more may lower your blood pressure and blood-sugar levels and require a review of your medication regime.

IN SUMMARY

Breathing retraining can be a wonderful tool to help you take back control of your breathing, of your physiology, and your physical and mental wellbeing. However, when you change your breathing, it is vital that you see your doctor for review and advice regarding any serious health conditions you have and any changes in prescribed treatments and medication.

CHAPTER 25

Hold-ups to improvement

If your progress is slow, use this list to help identify issues that may be causing or reinforcing disordered breathing, or preventing you from moving forward. I have found the most common issues to be:

1. Going at the changes too hard; being too controlling and creating more stress for yourself.
2. Eating a high-sugar/high-starch diet, which is also too low in natural fat and protein.
3. Excess alcoholic, caffeinated and sugary drinks.
4. Persistent, unconscious sighing, yawning and mouth breathing.
5. Fully exhaling – emptying or pushing air out of your lungs.
6. Slumped posture.
7. Holding your stomach in all the time.
8. Insufficient physical exercise.
9. Poor breathing control and mouth breathing while exercising.
10. Sleeping flat on your back with your mouth open.
11. Overheating in bed.
12. Over-sleeping.
13. Exposure to a lot of stress.
14. Gasping inhales through your mouth during speech.
15. Not persevering long enough with breathing retraining.
16. An oral/lip muscle function problem that makes nose breathing difficult.
17. Presence of chronic inflammation or infection in your body, such as in the nose, sinuses, tonsils, mouth or teeth, or tinea or candida.
18. Gut disorders, diagnosed or undiagnosed.

19. A medical condition you have, and/or medication(s) you take which affect your breathing/increase your breathing rate, or affect your ability to concentrate and retain information.

What to do? If you have identified something in this list where you think change is still needed and it is something you can address yourself, give it a try. You could revisit the chapter on food and its effects on breathing (Chapter 9). You could take the action steps towards healthy breathing habits that are not yet second nature. You could get help from a breathing educator. If symptoms of anxiety are still interfering with your daily life, consult your doctor or mental health professional.

In the case of point one above, see The Three Day Holiday page 158.

If point 7 is an issue and you regularly attend exercise classes that involve tensing of the abdominal muscles, you need to stop these exercises until you retrain your breathing. To break a pattern of rigidity, or 'over-engagement' in the abdominal muscles (it drives upper-chest breathing), keep practising the instructions in Chapters 14, 16 and 18 for healthy habits three, five and seven. Or get a copy of the Breathing Exercise Instruction Audio (see Learning Resources page 201). Get your breathing right first as described in this book and on the CD, then go back to your classes and substitute relaxed diaphragm breathing with a normal tidal volume into the movements and postures you practice.

A speech pathologist or orofacial myologist may help with point 16.

For points 17 and 18, see the appropriate healthcare professional(s) for investigation and treatment. Inflammation anywhere in the body can increase your breathing rate; various illnesses of the digestive system can affect your mind as well as your breathing. If you're having trouble normalising your breathing, get yourself checked out for inflammatory conditions of the digestive tract, candida, parasites, and gut dysbiosis. This is a condition where the natural flora of the gut is thrown out of balance, such as when antibiotics are taken. When there is an imbalance between the 'good' and 'bad' bacteria or flora in your gastrointestinal tract, digestion, colon pH balance, production of B vitamins and vitamin K, nutrient absorption, toxin excretion, immune function, and breathing may all be disturbed. A naturopath or nutritional therapist may be able to get your digestive system functioning well again. Taking a probiotic supplement or fermented dairy foods like kefir and good quality unsweetened yogurt, naturally rich in healthy probiotic bacteria, can help to restore good gut function and health.

FINDING TIME TO PRACTISE

If this is the problem, please review the suggested practice times and ways to blend better breathing into your normal day. If you can find the time to read a novel for 20 minutes or polish your car, you can find the time to practise better breathing. Playing one or two tracks of the Breathing Exercise Instruction Audio last thing at night and first thing in the morning can be a great way to 'bookend' your day for better breathing and relaxation.

CHAPTER 26

Taking it further

The basics of breathing retraining as they appear in this book can be safely self-taught and can deliver wonderful results within a very short time. So often I have seen the instruction in just breathing awareness, posture and more gentle breathing ('shrinking your cloud') produce dramatic improvements in total symptom scores within a few days. Being your own teacher can also be a bonus to those with anxiety, because you can set the pace to suit yourself, and practise in your own time and in your own space. The potential of the program in this book is immense.

A book, however, provides general information. A breathing educator/teacher can tailor that information to the specific needs of an individual and take into account the broader circumstances such as complicated health conditions. It is certainly beyond the scope of this book to try to match what a good teacher can do.

THE BENEFITS OF WORKING WITH A BREATHING EDUCATOR

Undergoing breathing retraining with an experienced breathing educator may assist you to go faster and further in normalising your breathing. When a teacher observes your breathing and posture, and takes your personal health history into account, they can choose the best approach for you from among the various exercises and techniques available. Their supervision ensures exercises are done correctly. Where appropriate, they can use intensive training or 'stronger' techniques.

Even when working with a breathing educator, not all students are able to completely normalise their breathing. There may be anatomical or pathological reasons for falling short of the ideal, or they may stop their practice before their breathing is fully normalised. However, any improvement can make a tremendous difference to quality of life.

A study has shown that three months after beginning breathing retraining (the Buteyko Method), the average minute volume for a group of chronic asthmatics had reduced significantly from 14 litres per minute to 9.6 litres per minute.[26.1] Although this indicates a degree of over-breathing still occurring at that stage, nonetheless, the results were extraordinary: an average 71 per cent reduction in symptoms, 96 per cent reduction in use of bronchodilators and 49 per cent reduction in steroid preventative medication.

At the three-month point, the breathing training group was a long way from where they started, and a long way ahead of the control group. The latter, on a conventional asthma management regime and 'standard' breathing/relaxation exercises, did not improve in any aspect and were unable to reduce their medications.

FINDING A BREATHING EDUCATOR

Although the popularity of breathing retraining – or breathing re-education as it is sometimes known – is spreading, as a specific field of healthcare it is still relatively unknown. Within the public health system, you may find breathing retraining programs, but they are far from being universally available. In most westernised countries, breathing retraining is available privately from individual breathing educators who may consult and teach one-on-one, in small-group classes and via Skype. See Learning Resources – Websites, page 202 for professional associations for breathing educators.

The enormous need throughout the world for breathing retraining, the lack of information about it and the current undersupply of proficient breathing educators, all spurred me on to develop resources to make breathing retraining more accessible. Resources through BreatheAbility International include books, audio (CD and MP3) and online courses, and training programs for health professionals. See Learning Resources page 201.

BREATHING GADGETS – YES OR NO?

How about a gadget, an app or a device to train your breathing? Sure, there are plenty available and maybe for some they are the answer. But for long-term benefit you need to have a real 'feel' for your breathing, feel when it's going 'off' and importantly, know how to fix it. Otherwise what happens if you are in a panic situation and you are dependent on an app to tell you what to do because you can't think straight? Or the internet is down, or you can't find your tablet or smart phone, or it has run out of battery?

What if the only way you could have good posture and good breathing is by sitting on a Swiss ball, but yours rolled against the heater and melted? What if you can't check your breathing without a capnometer (a carbon dioxide measuring device) and you can't afford one? What if you went for a 'user-passive' device that changes your breathing while you breathe through a mask and watch television – do you really know how to breathe when you are not using it? If you stop using these devices after a while, will you hold better breathing? Will you have a feel for what normal breathing is?

The plethora of breathing devices and electronic applications out there feeds into the culture of reliance on technology. And yet we need to consider that overuse of screen technology devices may have been a significant contributor to the slumped, open-mouth posture and poor breathing seen in many of today's children that has them headed towards needing orthodontic correction and maybe a behavioural or sleep disorder.

Yes, breathing training classes or using this book require time, but they train you to look after yourself and your breathing anywhere, anytime. They give you skills that will become second nature, to draw on automatically in crisis situations because you have practised them and *blended them into normal life*. So you have them to use when you are on top of a high mountain, on stage or there is a power failure.

CHAPTER 27

Summary, plan and learning guide

This list includes the nine healthy breathing habits and extra strategies you may find helpful. Tick them off when you have accomplished them.

Breathe correctly – develop all nine healthy breathing habits

- Be aware of your breathing; watch it throughout the day.
- Breathe more gently; visualise your 'cloud' shrinking.
- Nose breathe during the day and during sleep.
- Walk, move at the pace at which you can comfortably nose breathe.
- Sit, stand and walk in the relaxed upright *coathanger posture.*
- Keep your breathing regular and smooth.
- Breathe with your diaphragm, using your *soft gold band.*
- Breathe slowly.
- Breathe silently, gently, 'invisibly'; practice *hibernating.*
- Control or slow down your speech; take the in-breaths through your nose.
- Breathe in and out through your nose and using your diaphragm when exercising.
- Listen to the breathing exercise instruction audio two to three times a day for three weeks.

Reduce and relieve symptoms with breath control

- Use *short breath holds* to reduce blocked nose, sighing, yawning and coughing.
- Use the panic control exercises – 3 x 3 and 3-to-5-and-back-again versions of short breath holds, or the therapeutic walk when you feel stressed or anxious, or for insomnia.

Eat healthily

- Eat when you are hungry and in moderate quantities.
- Eat balanced proportions of protein, fat and carbohydrate in every meal or snack.
- Avoid foods and food combinations that rapidly increase your blood sugar.

Lifestyle

- Get some sunshine and fresh air.
- Exercise at least three times a week
- Relax.
- Manage stress.
- Get enough quality sleep.
- Seek professional help for emotional issues.

Be checked for underlying disorders

- Digestive health, enzymes, stomach acid and gut microflora.
- Iron, hormone, thyroid, blood sugar irregularities.

CHAPTER 28

Conclusion

Getting your breathing right early in your journey to health can save a lot of time and expense going down long, convoluted and sometimes dead-end paths. But it is never too late to change. The level of calmness, control and vitality you achieve when you get your breathing right has its source at a deep level of your nervous system, a shift that could never be brought about by medication.

Breathing retraining works, and together with some simple lifestyle changes it can relieve or prevent much of the mental, emotional and physical suffering endured by so many poor breathers. And we need to do something about it NOW. Anxiety affects one in 13 worldwide. The condition is rampant across cultures and age groups.

I have several hopes for this book and the first is for you. I hope that it inspires in you a lifelong commitment to breathing correctly, and that with that change you go on to enjoy a lifetime of calm and ease, quiet, restful sleep, abundant health and vitality, and a wonderful sense of wellbeing.

In addition, I hope that the message of this book spreads far and wide to parents everywhere so that they can know the value and importance of proper breathing for their children's mental and physical health and wellbeing.

I wish for you the very best, for *every breath you take.*

PASS IT FORWARD

Many people have told me that their lives have been transformed forever because of changing the way they breathe. It was often a family member, neighbour or work colleague who told them about my work or my books. More than once I have heard it was a complete stranger, someone beside them on a park bench, in the adjacent bed in hospital, a passing motorist who pulled over to the roadside where they had stopped in a panic.

Pass this information on and be part of a movement towards a happier, healthier, more nature-based society, where our bodies work as nature so magnificently designed them to.

FREQUENTLY ASKED QUESTIONS

Q: I have been told I have a brain chemistry imbalance. How could breathing exercises help?

A: Your brain chemistry does not go haywire for no reason. It is directly affected by the way you breathe. The carbon dioxide level in your blood is the primary determinant of your body's chemical balance (pH). The bottom line is you are going to have much more normal and more stable brain chemistry if you gain control of your breathing.

Q: What is the connection between breathing and anxiety and panic attacks?

A: Acute hyperventilation or 'over-breathing' is an obvious feature during a panic attack. You dump out lots of carbon dioxide. While less noticeable, the chronic form of over-breathing is very common in people with anxiety and panic disorders. Research has found people with panic disorders breathe 12 L a minute at rest when it should be 5 L. Chronic over-breathing alters carbon dioxide levels and blood chemistry and contributes to hyper-arousal of your nervous system (fight-or-flight), with too much of the stress hormones adrenaline and cortisol being produced. Chronic over-breathing is like having your foot on the accelerator all the time. You are 'primed' and trigger-happy.

Q: How does breathing retraining help people with anxiety and panic attacks?

A: Breathing retraining aims to correct your baseline breathing pattern – bring your breathing and blood gas chemistry back to normal to prevent symptoms and attacks. It shows you how to breathe correctly all the time, to access the 'parasympathetic' or relaxation branch of your autonomic nervous system. Normal breathing and controlled breathing is very calming. It's a natural sedative. Breathing retraining also shows you how to keep control of your breathing when you are under stress. It's a wonderful tool to have to stay calm, relaxed and in control in stressful situations and to get off to sleep.

Q: Is breathing retraining any use when my nose is nearly always blocked?
A: Yes. Noses are often blocked because of irritation, dehydration and inflammation – all side-effects of chronic over-breathing, the faulty breathing habit most often seen in people with anxiety. When you learn to breathe correctly, airway irritation reduces. In over 20 years of breathing retraining, I have rarely seen a nose that won't at least partially clear within the first five minutes of beginning to change a poor breathing pattern.

Q: I get panicky when I shut my mouth – is breathing retraining even possible for me?
A: Many people cannot tolerate 'forcing' nose breathing by trying to keep their mouth closed. They become claustrophobic or feel uncomfortable, as though they are suffocating. The *BreatheAbility* style of breathing retraining taught here *gradually* 'reconditions' you, so you can achieve comfortable nose breathing at your own pace. The initial step may be to breathe more gently through your mouth or to adjust your posture. (See Chapters 5, 13, and 14.)

Q: If breathing retraining is so good, why did my doctor only recommend medication/psychotherapy/counselling to me?
A: There is a general lack of knowledge about breathing pattern dysfunction. Most doctors are not well informed about the principles of breathing retraining, and observation and assessment of a patient's habitual breathing pattern is not part of standard medical diagnosis. Most doctors have simply not considered breathing retraining as an option for their patients. Has your doctor ever assessed your baseline breathing pattern? Breathing

retraining is a logical, scientific and conservative approach to the management of breathing-related disorders. Your doctor should be no more reluctant to suggest you improve your breathing habits than to recommend other self-help approaches such as meditation, yoga, avoiding alcohol, losing weight, and getting regular exercise.

Q: How long does it take to feel a difference with breathing retraining?
A: People usually notice benefits such as being more relaxed, having a lower heart rate, less nasal congestion, and quieter and easier breathing within hours (or even just minutes). Better sleep is often reported right from the first night. 'The best sleep in decades' is a frequent comment.

Q: I learnt breathing exercises (e.g. in yoga, Pilates, counselling) and felt dizzy/breathless/tired/anxious afterwards. Why would breathing retraining exercises be any different?
A: If the breathing exercises you learnt involved big, deep in-breaths with full exhales, particularly if by mouth, then likely you caused a shortfall in carbon dioxide in your blood. This can result in blood vessels narrowing and reducing the amount of oxygen that gets through to your brain and muscle cells. Thus dizziness, anxiety, panic, breathlessness, and fatigue may occur. The difference with a breathing retraining program as described in this book is that you are taught to breathe normally – at the correct rate and volume – so that you keep your blood chemistry in balance. This is essential in allowing the oxygen in your blood to actually get to the cells where it is needed. This is vastly different from a focus on getting as much oxygen into your lungs as possible.

Q: Does it take a lot of time? I don't have time to do breathing exercises.
A: Why not? You are breathing all the time, aren't you? You can make changes in your breathing any time in the day – while you watch television, walk to the car, stand in a queue, sit on a plane or a train. This is one of the advantages for busy people of breathing retraining over other exercise programs. Breath awareness and breath management can be applied during any activity. If you can do this for just a few days, you will be a changed

person. You have around 16,000 opportunities a day to make a difference.

Q: Do I have to stop other treatments?

A: No, you can practise breathing correctly while you continue to use medications and appliances, attend counselling sessions and so on. In fact, improving your breathing can help you get more from other therapies. Ultimately though, if you return your breathing to normal, your requirement for other treatments may change and then you can discuss your situation with your doctor.

GLOSSARY

ACRONYMS

CPAP	continuous positive airway pressure
COPD	chronic obstructive pulmonary disorder
ECG	electrocardiogram
IBS	irritable bowel syndrome
OCD	obsessive compulsive disorder

adenoids – gland-like tissue at the back of the nasal passage.

alveoli – the little air sacs in the lungs where gas exchange occurs.

anaerobic metabolism – the creation of energy through the combustion of carbohydrates when there is insufficient oxygen for energy production.

anatomy – the science of studying the structure and shape of an organism.

apnoea – cessation of breathing; sleep apnoea. A condition where breathing repeatedly stops or significantly decreases during sleep.

autonomic nervous system – the part of the nervous system that regulates involuntary action, as of the intestines, heart and glands. It is divided into the sympathetic nervous system and the parasympathetic nervous system.

baseline breathing pattern – a person's usual, everyday, unconscious or habitual way of breathing.

Bohr effect – states that the release of oxygen from the haemoglobin in the blood into the tissues is dependent on the level of carbon dioxide in the blood.

breathing-control centre – see 'respiratory centre'.

breathing pattern disorder – a combination of different signs and symptoms that may be seen when there is disturbance in normal breathing function.

breathing retraining – the specific discipline where the primary goal is to normalise each aspect of the breathing pattern for all situations.

capnometer – a device used to measure the amount of carbon dioxide in the exhaled breath.

central sleep apnoea – when breathing repeatedly stops during sleep because the brain temporarily stops sending signals to the muscles that control breathing.

chronic obstructive pulmonary disease (COPD) – a lung disease; it includes chronic bronchitis (a long-term cough with mucus) and emphysema (involves inflammation of the airways, damage to the alveoli, and loss of elasticity in the lungs). The main symptom is breathlessness.

cognitive behaviour therapy – challenges faulty thinking patterns that cause people to view themselves, their future and the world negatively.

diaphragm – the major breathing muscle.

dysfunctional breathing – abnormality in breathing function; chronic or intermittent changes in breathing pattern causing respiratory and non-respiratory complaints such as anxiety, light headedness, shortness of breath, throat tightness and fatigue.

fight-or-flight – the 'fight-or-flight' centre of the brain is part of the autonomic nervous system. The fight-or-flight response is where your body reacts to an emergency situation or a threat with an adrenaline, cortisol and blood-sugar surge.

hypercapnia – carbon dioxide level above normal.

hyperventilation – breathing an amount of air that is excessive in relation to metabolism and which creates a deficiency of carbon dioxide.

hypocapnia – carbon dioxide level below normal, due to an imbalance between the production and elimination of carbon dioxide.

hypopnoea – under-breathing; breathing that is shallower or slower than normal.

hypoventilation – insufficient ventilation to meet the body's oxygen requirements and to eliminate the appropriate amount of carbon dioxide.

hypoxia – deficiency of oxygen.

insomnia – inability to sleep or difficulty in falling or staying asleep.

insulin resistance - a condition in which cells fail to respond normally to the hormone insulin; the cells are unable to use it as effectively.

irritable bowel syndrome (IBS) – recurrent abdominal pain and diarrhoea or constipation, often associated with stress. IBS is thought to be a disorder of the interaction between the brain and gastrointestinal tract.

lactic acid – a chemical formed when sugars are broken down for energy in the absence of sufficient oxygen.

metabolic rate – the rate at which energy is used by the organism.

metabolism – the chemical processes occurring within a living cell or organism that are necessary for the maintenance of life.

mindfulness – the state of being conscious or aware of thoughts, feelings, bodily sensations, and surroundings; of 'being in the present'.

minute volume – the total volume of air breathed per minute.

neuroplasticity – the brain's ability to reorganise itself by forming new neural connections. Neuroplasticity allows the neurons (nerve cells) in the brain to adjust their activities in response to new situations and experiences and to compensate for injury and disease.

neurotransmitter – a chemical substance that allows 'messages' to be carried along nerve pathways.

obstructive sleep apnoea – a condition where breathing repeatedly stops or significantly decreases during sleep because of a narrowing or obstruction in the upper airway, typically in the pharynx.

occlusion (in dentistry) – the alignment of the teeth of the upper and lower jaws when brought together.

over-breathing – breathing an amount of air that is excessive in relation to metabolism and which creates a deficiency of carbon dioxide.

palate – the palate, in the roof of the mouth, consists of the hard palate and the soft palate. The hard palate at the front of the mouth contains bone.

paradigm – a view accepted by an individual or a society as a clear example, model or pattern of how things work.

pH – a measure of the acidity or alkalinity of a solution.

pharynx – the wall of the throat behind the nose and tongue.

physiology – the study of normal body function; the science that deals with the mechanical, physical and biochemical functions and processes of the body.

polyps – small sac-like growths of inflamed mucous membrane in the nose or sinuses.

psychotherapy – the treatment of a mental health disorder by psychological methods, by talking with a psychiatrist, psychologist or other mental health provider.

psychotropic (medications) – act on the brain and are used to control behaviour and mood. They include antidepressants, sedatives, anti-psychotics, mood stabilisers, and attention-deficit hyperactivity disorder medications.

respiratory centre – the 'breathing-control centre', the special group of cells (carbon dioxide receptors) in your brainstem that regulates the rate and depth of breathing to keep the carbon dioxide concentration in your arterial blood at the optimal level (set point) so that all bodily processes function well. It determines the signals to be sent to the respiratory muscles.

respiration rate – the number of complete breaths taken per minute.

restless legs – a feeling of uneasiness and restlessness in the legs, generally in the evening and after going to bed, but can occur during the day .

rhinitis – inflammation of the mucous membranes of the nose.

serotonin – a naturally occurring chemical in the brain (a neurotransmitter) that is responsible, in part, for regulating brain functions.

signs – any indication of a condition that can be objectively observed.

sinusitis – inflammation of the sinuses.

sleep-disordered breathing – abnormal pattern of breathing occurring during sleep.

smooth muscle – sometimes called involuntary muscle. A type of muscle found in many places in the body, including the walls of the airways and blood vessels.

soft palate – the soft part of the roof of the mouth; see 'palate'.

solar plexus – the area of the upper abdomen above the navel and below the lower end of the breastbone.

symptoms – subjective experiences; something consciously affecting the patient.

tidal volume – the volume of air inhaled and exhaled at each breath. Normal tidal volume is 500 ml.

tonsils – glands, situated in the throat.

CHAPTER REFERENCES AND RESOURCE MATERIALS

CHAPTER 2

2.1 http://www.beyondblue.org.au/index.aspx?link_id=2 Accessed 2/2/2013
Beyondblue, a national organisation working to address issues associated with depression, anxiety and related disorders in Australia.

2.2 'Trends in the utilisation of psychotropic medications in Australia from 2000 to 2011'. McGregor IS, Stephenson CP and Karanges E. *Aust N Z J Psychiatry* 2013; 47(1): 74-87.

2.3 http://www.health.harvard.edu/newsletters/Harvard_Womens_Health_Watch/
2008/July/Anxiety_and_physical_illness accessed 24/02/2013

2.4 http://www.who.int/whr/2001/main/en/chapter2/002g.htm
WHO World Health Report. 2001.

2.5 'Lifetime prevalence and age-of-onset distributions of DSM-IV disorders in the National Comorbidity Survey Replication'. Kessler R C, Berglund P, Demler O, Jin R, Merikangas KR and Walters EE. *Arch Gen Psychiatry* 2005; 62(6): 593-602.

2.6 'Asthma linked to psychiatric disorders'. Kuehn BM. *JAMA*. 2008; 299(2): 158-160.

2.7 'The effects of breathing-related sleep disorders on mood disturbances in the general population'. Ohayon MM. *J Clin Psychiatry*. 2003 Oct; 64(10): 1195-1200. http://www.ncbi.nlm.nih.gov/pubmed/14658968?dopt=AbstractPlus. Accessed 17/02/2013

2.8 'Phobic Anxiety and Risk of Coronary Heart Disease and Sudden

Cardiac Death Among Women'. Albert CM, Chae CU, Rexrode KM, Manson JE and Kawachi I. *Circulation* 2005; 111: 480-487.

2.9 'The cognitive behavioural model of irritable bowel syndrome: a prospective investigation of patients with gastroenteritis.' Spence, Moss-Morris R. *Gut* 2007; 56(8): 1066-1071. Epub 2007 Feb 26.

2.10 'Controversies surrounding the comorbidity of depression and anxiety in inflammatory bowel disease patients: a literature review'. Mikocka-Walus AA, Turnbull DA, Moulding NT, Wilson IG and Holtmann GJ. *Inflamm Bowel Dis.* 2007; 13(2): 225-234.

CHAPTER 3

3.1 Quote by Dr Peter Breggin in online article 'Are There Biochemical Imbalances?' http://www.cchrint.org/psychdrugdangers/TheChemicalImbalanceMyth.html. Accessed 24/02/2013. Peter R Breggin and David Cohen are co-authors of: *Your Drug May Be Your Problem.* Perseus Publishing, USA 1999 ISBN: 0-7382-0348-3

3.2 'Serotonin and Depression: A Disconnect between the Advertisements and the Scientific Literature'. Lacasse JR and Leo J. 2005. *PLoS Med* 2(12): e392. doi:10.1371/journal.pmed.0020392. Accessed 03/04/2013

3.3 *Breathe Well, Be Well.* Fried R. 1999; John Wiley & Sons.

3.4 'Hypocapnia'. Laffey JG and Kavanagh BP.*N Engl J Med.* 2002; 347: 43–53.

CHAPTER 4

4.1 'Breathing patterns. 2. Diseased subjects'. Tobin MJ, Chadha TS, Jenouri G, Birch SJ, H Gazeroglu HB and Sackner MA. *Chest* 1983; 84(3): 286-294

4.2 'Panic disorder and respiratory variables'. Pain MC, Biddle N and Tiller JW. *Psychosom Med.* 1988; 50(5) 541-548.

4.3 'Physiologic instability in panic disorder and generalized anxiety disorder'. Wilhelm FH, Trabert W and Roth WT. *Biol Psychiatry.* 2001; 49: 596-605.

4.4 *Buteyko Method: The experience of implementation in medical practice.* Buteyko KP. Kiev, Moscow, Novosibirsk. 1990. Patriot Press, Moscow

4.5 'Hyperventilation: the tip of the iceberg'. Lum LC. *Journal of Psychosomatic Research* 1975; 19: 375–383.

RESOURCES FOR PHYSIOLOGICAL NORMS

Review of Medical Physiology. Ganong WF. 6th ed. 1973; Lange Medical Publications.

Human Physiology. Vander A, Sherman J, and Luciano D. 5th ed. 1990; McGraw Hill, New York.

Human Physiology - From Cells to Systems. Sherwood L. 4th ed. 2001; Brooks/Cole, CA, USA. P. 451-458

CHAPTER 6

6.1 'Panic disorder and respiratory variables'. Pain MC, Biddle N and Tiller JW. *Psychosom Med.* 1988; 50(5) 541-548.

6.2 'Breathing patterns. 2. Diseased subjects'. Tobin MJ, Chadha TS, Jenouri G, Birch SJ, H Gazeroglu HB and Sackner MA. *Chest* 1983; 84(3):286-294

6.3 'Hyperventilation: benign symptom or harbinger of catastrophe?' Hanashiro PK. *Postgrad Med.* 1990; 88:191-193.

6.4 'Hypocapnia'. Laffey JG and Kavanagh BP.*N Engl J Med.* 2002; 347: 43–53.

6.5 'Basilar Artery Response to Hyperventilation in Panic Disorder'. Ball S and Shekhar A. *Am J Psychiatry* 1997; 154:1603-1604.

6.6 'Treatment of mast cells with carbon dioxide suppresses degranulation via a novel mechanism involving repression of increased intracellular calcium levels'. Strider JW, Masterson CG and Durham PL. *Allergy* 2011; 66: 341–350.

6.7 *Relaxation Revolution: The Science and Genetics of Mind Body Healing.* Benson H and Proctor W. 2010; Simon and Schuster, New York.

CHAPTER 7

7.1 'Hypocapnia'. Laffey JG and Kavanagh BP. *N Engl J Med.* 2002; 347: 43–53.

7.2 'Treatment of mast cells with carbon dioxide suppresses degranulation via a novel mechanism involving repression of increased intracellular calcium levels'. Strider JW, Masterson CG and Durham PL. *Allergy* 2011; 66: 341–350.

7.3 'Sleep disorders linked to depression in young women'. Amy Corderoy, health editor, Sydney Morning Herald, April 2013

7.4 'Control of breathing in obstructive sleep apnoea and in patients with the overlap syndrome'. Radwan L, Maszczyk Z, Koziorowski A, Koziej M, Cieslicki J, Sliwinski P and Zielinski J. *Eur Respir J.* 1995; 8(4): 542–545.

7.5 'Sleep Apnoea and Breathing Retraining: To what extent is the Buteyko Institute Method of breathing retraining effective for sleep apnoea? A survey of Buteyko Institute practitioners' experiences with clients suffering from sleep apnoea'. Birch M. 2012. Report is available at www.buteyko.info/latest_buteyko_news.asp?newsid=27

7.6 *Relief from Snoring and Sleep Apnoea.* Graham T. 2012; Penguin Group, Camberwell Australia.

7.7 'Hyperventilation syndrome: A diagnosis begging for recognition' (Topics in Primary Care Medicine). Magarian GJ, Middaugh DA and Linz DH. *West J Med.* 1983; 138: 733–736.

7.8 'Hyperventilation: the tip of the iceberg'. Lum LC. *Journal of Psychosomatic Research* 1975; 19: 375–383.

7.9 *Breathe Well, Be Well.* Fried R. 1999; John Wiley & Sons.

CHAPTER 8

8.1 'Ventilatory responses to inhaled carbon dioxide, hypoxia, and exercise in idiopathic hyperventilation'. Jack S, Rossiter HB, Pearson MG, Ward SA, Warburton CJ and Whipp BJ. *Am J Respir Crit Care Med.* 2004; 170(2): 118–125.

8.2 'Effort syndrome – hyperventilation and reduction of anaerobic threshold'. Nixon PGF. *Biofeedback Self.* 1994; 19(2): 155–169.

8.3 'The role of hyperventilation - hypocapnia in the pathomechanism of panic disorder'. Sikter A, Frecska E, Braun IM, Gonda X and Rihmer Z. *Rev Bras Psiquiatr.* 2007; 29(4): 375–379.

CHAPTER 9

9.1 'Defusing the health care time bomb'. Lustig RH. San Francisco Chronicle January 5, 2013. Accessed 12/1/2013. http://www.sfgate.com/opinion/article/Defusing-the-health-care-time-bomb-4168827.php#ixzz2HhyN8ScV

9.2 Chowdhury R et al Ann Intern Med. 2014; 160(6): 398-406. doi:10.7326/M13-1788

9.3 *The Omega Diet.* Simopolous AP and Robinson J. 1999; HarperCollins, New York.

9.4 'Cholesterol, Statins, and Brain Function: A Hypothesis from a Molecular Perspective'. Shin Yeon-Kyun. Interdisciplinary Bio Central 2009; 1:2, 1-4 • DOI: 10.4051 / ibc.2009.1.0002 . (page 2)

9.5 'Demonstration of an association among dietary cholesterol, central serotonergic activity, and social behavior in monkeys'. Kaplan JR, Shively CA, Fontenot MB, Morgan TM, Howell SM, Manuck SB, Muldoon MF and Mann JJ. *Psychosom Med.* 1994; 56(6):479-484.

9.6 'Association of low serum total cholesterol with major depression and suicide'. Partonen T, Haukka J, Virtamo J, Taylor PR and Lonnqvist *J. Br J Psychiatry.* 1999; 175, 259-262.

9.7 'Cholesterol-Reducing Drugs May Lessen Brain Function'. *Science Daily*, Feb 2009; http://www.sciencedaily.com/releases/2009/02/090223221430.htm

9.8 'Major depressive disorder: probiotics may be an adjuvant therapy'. Logan AC and Katzman M. *Med Hypotheses.* 2005; 64(3):533-538.

9.9 'Dry Skin'. Cowan T (MD). The Weston A Price Foundation: Ask the Doctor 30 June 2000. Retrieved from www.westonaprice.org/ask-the-doctor/dry-skin.

9.10 'Salt your Way to Health'. Brownstein D, (MD) Salt Institute, www.saltinstitute.org

CHAPTER 10

10.1 'Persistent respiratory irregularity in patients with panic disorder'. Abelson JL, Weg JG, Nesse RM and Curtis GC. *Biol Psychiatry.* 1996; 39: 521-522.

10.2 'Blood, breath, and fear: A hyperventilation theory of panic attacks and agoraphobia'. Ley R. *Clin Psychol Rev.* 1985; 5: 271-285.

10.3 'Ventilatory physiology of patients with panic disorder'. Gorman JM, Fryer MR, Goetz R, Askanazi J, Liebowitz MR and Fryer AJ. *Arch Gen Psychiatry.* 1988; 45:31-39.

10.4 'Respiratory psychophysiology of panic disorder: three respiratory challenges in 98 subjects'. Papp LA, Martinez JM, Klein DF, Coplan JD, Norman RG, Cole R, de Jesus MJ, Ross D, Goetz R and Gorman JM. *Am J Psychiatry* 1997; 154:1557-1565.

10.5 'Panic disorder and respiratory variables'. Pain MC, Biddle N and Tiller JW. *Psychosom Med.* 1988; 50(5): 541-548.

10.7 'A controlled study of a breathing therapy for treatment of hyperventilation syndrome'. Grossman P, De Swart JC and Defares PB. *J Psychosom Res.* 1985; 29: 49–58.

10.8 'Buteyko breathing techniques in asthma: a controlled trial'. Bowler SD, Green A, Mitchell CA. MJA 1988; 169: 575–578.

10.9 'The Buteyko method increases end-tidal CO2 and decreases ventilatory responsiveness in asthma'. Borg B, Doran C, Giorlando F, Hartley MF, Jack S, Johns DP, Wolfe R, Cohen M, Abramson MJ. In the Australian and New Zealand Society of Respiratory Science Inc. Annual Scientific Meeting. (2004). http://anzsrs.org.au/asm2004abstracts.pdf

10.10 'Buteyko Breathing Technique Reduces Hyperventilation-Induced Hypocaponea (sic) and Dyspnoea after Exercise in Asthma'. Austin G et al. Am. J. Respir. Crit. Care Med. 2009; 179: A3409

10.11 'Changes in pCO2, symptoms and lung function of asthma patients during capnometry-assisted breathing training'. Ritz

T, Meuret AE, Wilhelm FH and Roth WT. *Appl Psychophysiol Biofeedback*. 2009; 34(1): 1–6.

10.12 SIGN 141 British guidelines on the management of asthma, October 2014 page 56. www.brit-thoracic.org.uk/document-library/clinical-information/asthma/btssign-asthma-guideline-2014/ accessed 9/07/2015

CHAPTER 19

19.1 *The Melba Method*. Dame Nellie Melba. 1926; Chappell & Co. p 10.

CHAPTER 24

24.1 'Breathing control lowers blood pressure'. Grossman E, Grossman A, Schein MH, Zimlichman R and Gavish B. *Journal of Human Hypertension* 2001; 15: 263–269.

24.2 'Buteyko breathing techniques in asthma: a controlled trial'. Bowler SD, Green A and Mitchell CA. *MJA* 1988; 169: 575–578.

24.3 'Buteyko breathing technique for asthma: An effective intervention'. McHugh P, Aitcheson F, Duncan B and Houghton F. *N Z Med J*. 2003; 116 (1187): U710.

CHAPTER 26

26.1 'Buteyko breathing techniques in asthma: a controlled trial'. Bowler SD, Green A and Mitchell CA. *MJA* 1988; 169: 575–578.

LEARNING RESOURCES

All information in this book is supplied in good faith, but you should also make your own enquiries and seek professional guidance if necessary before purchasing any of the products or services or undertaking any process, therapy or treatment.

BREATHEABILITY INTERNATIONAL AND TESSGRAHAM.COM

You can find help in the form of:

- information, articles, blogs, FAQ
- resources including books and audio learning aids
- workshops and events
- webinars and online courses.
- health professional training and mentoring programs

AIDS TO LEARNING

BREATHING EXERCISE INSTRUCTION AUDIO – CD AND MP3 FORMATS

If you prefer to learn through listening, you may benefit from our Breathing Exercise Instruction Audio. This companion product to the book is narrated by the author. Tess talks you through three levels of breathing exercise sessions, described in chapters 14, 16 and 18.

Go to Products at: BreatheAbility.com

WORKBOOK

Download the free workbook containing the Breathing Pattern Self-Assessment Table, the Dysfunctional Breathing Symptom Tracker, Observation Checklist and Meal Components Table.

Go to Products at: BreatheAbility.com

ONLINE BREATHING RETRAINING COURSE – BREATHEAWAY.COM.AU

The BreatheAway online breathing retraining course was created for those who prefer to learn through visual and auditory mediums. The course format is easy to follow, and easy to do. It is designed for people with busy lives. You can take it as fast or as slowly as you like. First results usually in under 24 hours.

4 hours content |12 lessons | Video, audio and graphics.

The online course is suitable for adults with asthma, nasal problems, chronic cough, anxiety, panic attacks, snoring, sleep apnoea, insomnia, breathlessness, or a desire for good health.

Information and online course registration: BreatheAway.com.au

WEBSITES

AUTHOR WEBSITE

TessGraham.com

BreatheAbility.com (Remember the 'e' at the end of 'Breathe')

ALEXANDER TECHNIQUE

Austat.org.au

Australian Society of Teachers of the Alexander Technique

BREATHING EDUCATORS PROFESSIONAL ASSOCIATIONS

breathingeducators.com

buteyko.info

Buteyko Institute of Breathing and Health (established Australia 1996)

buteykoeducators.org

Buteyko Breathing Educators Association. (established North America, 2010)

NUTRITION

westonaprice.org

The Weston A. Price Foundation with information on traditional diets, health principles and sourcing of quality nutrient dense foodstuffs.

RECOMMENDED READING

Nourishing Traditions. Sally Fallon with Mary Enig. 1999; New Trends Publishing, Inc. Washington DC.

Nutrition and Physical Degeneration. Dr Weston A. Price. 6th ed. 2004; Price–Pottenger Nutrition Foundation, La Mesa CA.

Gut and Psychology Syndrome. Dr Natasha Campbell McBride. 2010; Medinform Publishing UK.

Changing Habits, Changing Lives. Cyndi O'Meara. 2007; Penguin Group Australia.

Sweet Poison. David Gillespie. 2010; Penguin Group Australia.

Shut Your Mouth and Save your Life (1870). George Catlin. 2009; reprint; Kessinger Publishing.

Relief from Snoring and Sleep Apnoea. Tess Graham. 2012; Penguin Group Australia.

Relief from Snoring and Sleep Apnea. Tess Graham. 2014; CreateSpace Amazon USA.

ACKNOWLEDGEMENTS

Firstly, I want to thank my family and my friends who are always there for me. My appreciation also to my book and chapter reviewers: Helen Best, Karen St Clair, Jessica Graham, Michael Stenning and Geraldine Perriam, and to my proof reader, Judy Conroy. The book is greatly enhanced because of your thoughtful input and constructive suggestions. I want to especially thank Michelle Taja Miller for her insightful contribution to the cover copy, and Fiona Sandilands and Cath Hutchison for wonderful suggestions and insights into the fine role of psychologists for people with anxiety disorders.

Thank you to Deborah Bradseth (cover and interior design) and to Mat Colley (illustrations), for your skill, creativity and patience. My thanks to my editor, Gail Tagarro, for her generous and accommodating manner, and the skill and polish she applied to the manuscript.

Finally, I am grateful to all my clients whose enthusiasm, commitment and willingness to take responsibility for their health inspired me to produce this work. Their individual stories, which they so willingly shared in order to help others, have been a valuable input and make this book so real to its readers.

ABOUT THE AUTHOR

Tess Graham graduated from the University of New South Wales with a science degree (anatomy and physiology), followed by a post-graduate qualification in physiotherapy through Sydney University. From a young age, two of her three children suffered from asthma and relied on an arsenal of medications, nebulisers and puffers to relieve their symptoms. The traditionally prescribed breathing exercises used by physiotherapists did not help in asthma episodes.

After seven years of researching and trialing medical and natural health methods, Tess discovered the work of Ukrainian-born doctor, Konstantin Buteyko. His method of *breathing retraining* worked. Her children immediately experienced relief from asthma. Soon they became robust, healthy and symptom-free. They no longer required medication. Tess saw the broad potential of breathing retraining to help not only people with asthma but also those with anxiety, sleep disorders, nasal problems, any form of breathlessness, and those seeking general wellbeing and improved capacity for exercise. Tess became accredited in breathing retraining and established Australia's first dedicated breathing clinic in 1993, in Canberra, Australia.

Over the last two decades Tess has further developed the art of breathing retraining and has delivered her ground-breaking BreatheAbility programs to more than 6,000 people, with extraordinary and consistent success. She works on the premise that good health is not meant to be complicated, that the human body is capable of achieving and maintaining health as long as it has a knowledgeable and proficient driver at the control. The most fundamental skill set you need as the driver is the ability to breathe well. Teaching people to do so has been her life's work.

Many of the exercises and concepts in this book were created by Tess specifically to help people with anxiety. Her unique style of breathing retraining is profoundly and rapidly effective while being simple, gentle, stress-free, and easily adapted into busy lives.

Tess is the author of *Relief from Snoring and Sleep Apnoea* (Penguin Aus edition) and *Relief from Snoring and Sleep Apnea* (US edition). It has been translated into Chinese (Chien Hsing Publishing Company, Taipei) and Italian (Edizioni Mediterranee, Rome). Tess lectures extensively to medical, health professional, corporate and lay audiences in Australia and abroad. She lives in Canberra.

TESS GRAHAM - TRAINER

After 25 years in clinical practice, developing her unique style of breathing retraining and publishing two books, Tess now trains and mentors other health professionals.

Her training courses are highly sought after by physiotherapists, psychologists, midwives, and other therapists, by yoga, Pilates and fitness trainers, and by dental health professionals with an interest in airway and sleep issues. Tess's programs have immediate clinical application, allowing practitioners to enhance their work with breath within their modality, or to implement the breathing retraining process with their clients.

To find out more visit: BreatheAbility.com/Training

TESS GRAHAM - SPEAKER

Tess is a world authority on what it takes to get a restful night's sleep, to wake refreshed and have a sense of calm, energy and focus all day. For over two decades, Tess has delivered informative, relevant and practical programs that have enabled thousands to breathe better, sleep better, and be better.

This is because when Tess speaks about breathing, people change. They change what they think about breathing, and they change the way they breathe. When they change the way they breathe, their experience of sleep and wellbeing changes. So too does their capacity for work, life and play.

Tess speaks on the following topics:

SO YOU THINK YOU CAN BREATHE?

- Myth-busting – common breathing practices that may do more harm than good
- The 3 key breathing habits essential for good health and quality sleep
- Take-away strategies to improve energy, fitness and productivity

BREATHE WELL, SLEEP WELL

- How to breathe by day so you breathe silently and easily at night
- The missing link to a natural solution for snoring and sleep apnoea
- The 3 keys to restful sleep and energy all day

BREATHE CALM, COOL AND IN CONTROL

- How faulty breathing revs you up and stresses you out
- Simple strategies to relieve and prevent anxiety and panic attacks
- How to manage your physiology to stay calm under pressure and switch off and sleep well at night

Made in the USA
Middletown, DE
27 December 2020